FIND
YOUR
Weigh

What a refreshing and biblical look at our struggle with weight! Shellie brings hope and practicality to this health journey. The companion study guide adds an opportunity to take a deeper look into ourselves and provides guidelines with accompanying scriptures; helping us make changes in our thought life and choices about food. Shellie outlines powerfully how we can "Find our Weigh."

SANDRA MUNDIS – *Women's global networker serving alongside her husband Greg executive director of Assemblies of God World Missions.*

Are you tired of being on a dieting roller coaster? Are you looking for freedom from the condemnation and frustration of failing so many times? Then, "Find Your Weigh" is just what you need. Shellie talks about allowing God to change your mindset about food. It's an incredible journey of freedom from the struggles surrounding your weight and your self image. I encourage you to dive in and let God work through this incredible book and study.

BECCA KETTERLING – *Women's Pastor, River Valley Church*

Shellie Bowdoin has written a book that will change your thoughts on weight loss. This is not a "diet" book but a personal journey that will encourage you in the area of weight management. Shellie has combined practical principles, personal journaling and biblical insight that will enable you to establish life habits that will bring positive results in your health, weight and mindset. Shellie's desire is to help others and this book will accomplish that for many. I wholeheartedly recommend it.

DEBBIE COLE – *Host of the video series "Off-Script with Debbie" and Alongside Facilitator for the Northwest Ministry Network of the Assemblies of God*

As someone who knows the bondage of food and finding your worth in a number on the scale, Find Your Weigh was a breath of fresh air! Learning to really understand our thoughts around food is so important to healing that relationship, and Shellie outlines how to do it in an easy and practical way, rooted in Biblical truth. A must-read for anyone who struggles with food – which is all of us!

TAYLOR KISER – *Blogger at FoodFaithFitness.com*

Renew your mind . . .
walk in freedom

FIND
YOUR
Weigh

Shellie Bowdoin

SOURCE
ⓕ@sourcepublishing

ISBN 978–971–503–442–5 (Paperback)
ISBN 978–971–503–443–2 (EPub)
ISBN 978–971–503–444–9 (Mobi/Kindle)

First printing: 2016

SOURCE PUBLISHING
Division of ICI Ministries
www.iciphilippines.org

www.findyourweighbook.com

This book is dedicated to my little family: Sam, Jay, Emily, and Mary Kate. Even when no one else was around, our little unit has been a source of immeasurable joy and contentment. I am blessed.

SHELLIE BOWDOIN

Renew your mind...
walk in freedom

FIND
YOUR
Weigh

BIBLE STUDY
GUIDE

NINE SESSIONS

Contents

Foreword

IT'S DEEPER THAN A DIET . . . a lot deeper. I'm not sure if people a thousand years ago thought very much about body shape, but today, we're obsessed with it. We can't keep our eyes off of the models in magazine ads, movies stars on the red carpet, and the gorgeous people we see in the grocery store or just down the row in our church services. Then, we look at ourselves in the mirror.

Comparison kills. Immediately, our focus is riveted to something other than God. Longing raises our hopes that we too can achieve the perfect form, but just as quickly, shame crushes us because we can never quite get there. Many of us live in that netherworld between longing and shame, or more accurately, with a toxic combination of longing and shame all wrapped into one.

There has to be a better way to think about ourselves. There is, and Shellie Bowdoin has found it. For her, the quest for truth, peace, and joy comes out of her own painful experiences of dozens of failed diets. After years of struggle, she finally realized the forkful of food wasn't the problem. It was the lies she believed that clouded her thoughts and gave her misplaced hopes and dreams. As a pastor, I know her struggles are shared by countless others inside and outside the church.

Beliefs, Shellie explains, aren't sterile, academic propositions; they come loaded with powerful emotions. She looks back at three powerful, misguided beliefs that controlled her life:

- If I believed I was helpless, I acted helpless.

- If I believed certain foods were too yummy to resist, I didn't resist.

- If I believed that the role of food was to entertain me, then I turned to food every time my mind was not occupied by something else.

But we're not helpless, we live for a higher purpose than passing pleasure, and our minds can be occupied with the splendor of God's greatness and grace.

When we're obsessed with our bodies, we inevitably obsess about food, which leads to dashed hopes, hidden fears, and crushing shame that we just don't measure up. But as our hearts increasingly focus on God's character and we learn to relish our identity as His loved, forgiven, treasured children, we can find peace. The freedom God wants for us isn't found in trying harder but in trusting more. We can finally get off the rollercoaster of diets and discouragement, but only if we find a better ride. And we have.

In her book, bible study and videos, Shellie encourages us to have clear, reasonable goals, the grace to accept the body God has given us, and the patience to stay with healthy habits whatever our shape may be.

When Becca and I met Shellie on a trip to Thailand and heard her story and her dreams for her book, I immediately realized that she had put her finger on the heart issue that is so often missing in diet plans. Read this book, engage in the Bible study, listen to the Spirit of God whisper that you're God's dear child, and reorient your mind around the truth that you mean more to Him than the stars in the sky. With that perspective, your heart will be focused on the right thing . . . or more accurately, the right Person. You'll find a beautiful blend of freedom and determination.

If you struggle with longing and shame about your shape, you need Shellie's message. Don't miss it.

Rob Ketterling

Lead Pastor of River Valley Church, Burnsville, Minnesota
Author of *Front Row Leadership, Change before You Have To, and Fix It!*

Acknowledgements

I share a lot about myself in this book, but there are many things I do not say. Our lives are but a tapestry of shared moments and experiences of those we've known and walked with along the way.

My thoughts go first to my husband, Sam, who has stood by me, supported me and believed in me for well over half of my life now. We've grown up together and I have never doubted his love for a second.

I also give hugs to my extended family that has loved us and, at times, longed for us when we've been worlds apart. Your constant support gives me confidence because I know that I always have my own personal fan club…just because.

I think about all the women I have had the privilege of knowing. My heart has always been to inspire and motivate women to live lives of purpose. During the near-decade I lived in Laos, I met some great ladies from all over the world. My time as president of the Women's International Group was a pivotal time of stretching and preparation.

I've been blessed to have many special girlfriends along the way and each of them has sewn seeds deep within my heart. Whether or not we are together physically, these seeds continue to grow and bloom in my life.

There was always something in me that wanted to write a book, but I honestly never thought I would sit down to do it. My son's departure to college left an empty space in my heart and home for a while, but in the end I realize his absence was really the impetus for this whole journey. Thankfully, time does heal and the scars left behind help to make us just that much stronger.

I am so grateful that two kids, Jay and Mary Kate, call me mama. That is one of my most cherished titles I will wear for the rest of my life. They both make me a better person…and hopefully a little more patient one ☺.

When it comes to the nuts and bolts of this book, I could have never done it without the awesome Source Publishing team. All of you talented people have made me look so good and I am immensely grateful.

And lastly, I highly value God's hand on my life. If I have any piece of wisdom to share or insight to give, I fully acknowledge that it all comes from he who so richly bestows good things to those who seek him.

Shellie

"THEN YOU WILL KNOW THE TRUTH, AND
THE TRUTH WILL SET YOU FREE."

JOHN 8:32 (NIV)

Chapter 1

Introduction

PICTURES DON'T LIE. I LOOKED at my photo and was stunned by what I saw. When had I allowed myself to gain so much weight? Quite frankly, I had become accustomed to the number staring up at me from the dreaded platform of uncertainty, better known as a scale that sits in the corner of my bathroom floor. But somehow, I had convinced myself that women should just expect their weight to steadily increase.

After all, I had already tried, unsuccessfully, to lose weight on two separate occasions earlier that fall. Both times I had started out with drive and determination only to give up when the scale did not reward my Herculean efforts like I thought it should. Despite those failed attempts, that photograph brought on mental plans of the new diet I would launch yet again when the New Year came around.

How many times have you stood in this same place? Was it a picture or did you find yourself standing in the closet without one viable option to wear? We've all felt the frustration of pants that are too tight. There you are again, standing there, struggling to find clothes that still fit, only to conclude that your only real option is to put on the same go-to outfit you've been wearing everywhere… because it's the only thing that's still comfortable.

For me, this wake-up call rang out loudly and clearly on November, 2014. At first, it was inconceivable to even consider cutting back on food with the holiday season looming just around the corner. In fact, over the years, I had convinced myself that holiday weight gain was a foregone conclusion. After all, no one can resist the draw of rich holiday foods, right? That's when it hit me! I was not in charge of my body or my choices about food. Somewhere along the way, I had surrendered control of my eating to the pleasure of food and the taste of food.

I decided then and there that something had to change. I did not make an elaborate plan, nor did I go on a swan song binge before I hit the all-too-familiar diet road. I just made a decision that, from that day on, I was making the choices, and conscious choices at that, about the food I ate. It was time to find out what was behind my life-long rollercoaster ride with food. But this time, I wasn't just going to treat the symptomatic weight like I had always done in the past. I decided to explore my thinking about food and try to get a handle on it once and for all.

To be honest, I didn't have a clue what I was doing, but God did. For so many years I had approached my weight as merely a physical issue; something I had to "get a handle on." I got myself into a mess yet again, and it was up to me to summon the fortitude and willpower to get myself out. In essence, I'd pushed God to the sideline of my weight struggle. He had been waiting 30 years for me to finally call Him into the game.

The issue of weight and food is often taboo in Christian circles. We freely discuss everything else: jealousy, pride, depression, and other addictions, but food issues are conspicuously absent. Could it be that we don't like to bring attention to our food struggles because they're just so obvious? Unlike other struggles that can be hidden from prying eyes, many of us view our weight as an open advertisement of our failure, our inability to control our eating. Consequently, we feel that if we actually admit to our weakness, then we are obligated to fix it.

This mentality essentially closes us off from God's supernatural power. He assures us that His power is best manifested in our lives through our weaknesses. Paul actually wrote about this theme on nine different instances in the New Testament. God actually does some of His best transformative work by displaying his miraculous power through our weaknesses. He takes what we cannot do on our own and shows us that we were never meant to. He can transform our struggle into a tangible display of His intimate concern, but this can only happen when we admit that our weakness with food is much more than a physical issue we must overcome.

My Background

Prior to that November day, I had lost the same 25 to 40 pounds at least ten times in my life. In fact, I grew accustomed to having two different-sized wardrobes in my closet: one for the smaller me and another, for that inevitable time when the weight came back. Despite my efforts, there was always something in the back of my mind that just assumed I would eventually gain the weight back when my self-control took another nosedive.

My journey with food started when I was still in middle school. I was short and pudgy at a time when most of my friends gave little thought to food because of their quick pubescent metabolisms. Eventually, I did reach my full height in high school and the excess weight finally came off. Actually, in retrospect, I realize that growing out before growing up is a typical growth pattern in my family. My son actually matured in the same way.

However, the insecurity of being the "fat girl" in those early years undoubtedly affected how I viewed food. As a young teen, I really had little control over my weight, which was largely the result of a delayed growth spurt. In fact, I often secretly resented my friends who could eat anything they wanted and still maintain their slim be-jeaned figures while I was stuck shopping in the husky section.

The early insecurity I felt about my weight eventually permeated my whole mindset and relationship with food. In my youth, I had watched my peers eat whatever they wanted with seemingly no effect on their weight. They were all thin at a time in development when one's outward appearance was so highly valued, while I seemed powerless to do anything to change my weight. Somewhere along the line I convinced myself that I was powerless against the draw of food.

I developed an attitude of helplessness with food, convincing myself that I could not resist its lure or the constant cycle of weight gain and weight loss. Consequently, I have ridden the rollercoaster of weight loss and gain most of my life. While the insecurity of being an overweight teenager consistently motivated me to keep my weight within a specific range, I was never able to keep it in check for good. Despite my best intentions, food always seemed to win and I regularly felt guilt over my lack of self-control.

How Did This Book Come to Be?

I need to stop here to explain something foundational to this book. I didn't just suddenly figure out this link between my adolescent helplessness and my inability to resist food. It was a process and that's what *Find Your Weigh* is all about.

This is not just another diet book. Instead, it's a shared journey of self-discovery. I am not a professional medical specialist, a nutritionist, or a trained fitness professional. Instead, I'm a middle-aged child of Christ who finally stepped off of the weight roller coaster after going up and down my whole adult life.

Over the years, I've watched countless talk shows where medical professionals would explain how overeating typically has emotional roots, but I never internalized their message. I've watched fitness trainers with chiseled bodies tout the benefits of healthy eating, but I just figured they had genetically stronger constitutions than I did.

Somehow, even as a seminary-educated Christian, I missed the heart-mind connection that echoes through the pages of scripture. God's word consistently takes us back to the attitudes of the heart: the repository for all of our hopes, dreams, emotions, and desires. We are then expected to conform our minds to Christ by believing He is who He says He is and that He earnestly longs to walk with us through every area of our lives.

But, our hearts and minds have to work in tandem. What's more, we have to come to the point of acknowledging that no area of our life is beyond God's reach or unworthy of His attention. My weight wasn't my own physical problem to conquer; it was the very area where He desired to display His strength in the midst of my weakness.

I had to bring my food struggles into the light. In this transparent atmosphere, God helped me engage my heart and my mind to explore my thoughts and expectations. Only then, did I finally uncover what was behind my behavior with food. What's more, I understood, once and for all, that food is not my enemy, nor can food do anything to me that I don't allow.

Food Is a Vital Part of Life and Living

So, why is food such a big deal? For a person who struggles with weight, food can be an all-consuming proposition. Either you want it, you are upset that you ate too much of it (again), or you are making a plan to stay away from it.

Basically, the diet industry runs and thrives on this conundrum. It is banking on the fact you will eventually come to steps two and three. Then, they can swoop in to offer you the "solution" to your problem. Often these solutions involve staying completely away from all those "bad" foods that are the source of all your frustrations and pain.

What these diet solutions do not seem to address is how to extricate food from your memory, emotional framework, and cultural experience. Diets don't take into consideration the fact that food is a vital part of the human experience and a God-given blessing.

Food Deprivation Does Not Work

Each year, Americans shell out around $40 billion dollars on weight loss plans and products.[1] However, even after all the shakes are consumed and the calories are counted, The New England Journal of Medicine estimates that most people regain one-third of their weight back within the first year and return to their baseline within three to five years.[2] This is not ground-breaking news. We all know how hard it is to maintain weight loss after a diet. In fact, I bet a lot of you, like me, have experienced this firsthand.

For a person who struggles with weight, food can be an all-consuming proposition. Either you want it, you are upset that you ate too much of it (again), or you are making a plan to stay away from it.

The $40 billion Americans spend on diet plans each year is a weighty amount, for sure. But those billions represent aspirations rather than effort. Dieters who want to fit into thinner jeans for more than a few months or years need to find a diet plan that will fit into their lifestyle for just as long. If we're wasting billions of dollars on fruitless diets, it's likely the fault lies not with Jenny but with ourselves.[3]

Food Is an Integral Part of Our Memories and Cultural Identity

I think the biggest reason for our multiple diet failures is the fact that food and our cultural formation are two tightly bound concepts. Think back to some of your fondest childhood memories. Likely, you picture holidays or vacations you took with your family. Does food enter the equation? Of course it does: returning home on a college visit to see your mom's legendary chocolate cake awaiting you on the table, chatting on the back patio as steaks sizzled on the grill, or joining hands around a Thanksgiving table filled with your favorite foods.

I can't even count the times my family sat around the table reminiscing about our favorite family vacation only for the conversation to turn to some food that we all enjoyed. Food is linked with virtually all celebrations and milestones. Food is a vital part of our life experiences. We love nothing better than to sit around the table with those we love.

1 Timothy 4:4 reminds us that, "Everything God created is good and nothing is to be rejected if it is received with thanksgiving." If we are to take God at His word, then it's reasonable to assume that it is possible to engage our hearts in enjoying food for the blessing that it is while still utilizing our minds to eat it in a measured, focused way.

So, why do we think that we can just cut certain foods out of our lives, presumably for good, and then continue on as if they never existed? The Bible and modern-day research say we can't, so it's time to figure out a new way of thinking about food that actually includes eating all forms of it in a thoughtful, considered way. A new food mindset is the only way to actually have your cake and eat it too!

A new food mindset is the only way to actually have your cake and eat it, too!

What Can You Expect?

Over the course of my weight journey, I have concluded that weight loss is attainable at any age. I know there is a lot of expert advice out there. I have read countless websites and blogs written by dietitians, doctors, and ripped personal trainers. Undoubtedly, their advice and insights are extremely helpful. But sometimes, it just helps to talk to a normal, everyday person who has walked the same path.

Typically, my diet attempts were always preceded by excessive thought and self-chastisement. Then, I would embark on yet another diet to punish myself for past indiscretions. Each and every time, I would diet to get myself back on the "right" track and inevitably the right track would involve self-denial and self-deprivation. Does this sound familiar?

The real problem was that I was running in the wrong race. As God's child, I had access to a storehouse of resources. He literally had the A-team ready to run alongside me, but I had never considered asking for His help. It was time to tap into His life-giving power.

Have you also divorced your food struggle from the other emotional areas of your life and just figured you are on your own when it comes to your weight? In retrospect, I now recognize that's how I consistently approached my food struggles. Despite the fact that God's word is filled with promises that assure us of His abiding presence and His empowering strength in the midst of our weaknesses, most of us are determined to conquer our desire for food on our own.

Thankfully, I finally found a way to stop the lose/gain cycle and put myself in the driver's seat when it comes to food. Your journey will not be just like mine, but this book will walk you through my process and set you on a course of self-discovery.

I can honestly say the more out-of-control my weight was at different points in my life, the more I thought about it and the more weight issues would consume my thoughts and existence. Admittedly, there were times when I elevated food to such a degree that I often looked to it before I looked to God. Now, I am asking you to channel your thoughts about food into positive, meaningful change and allow God to focus your action toward developing food habits for a lifetime of future success with food.

In the process of *finding my weigh*, I have developed a series of tips and strategies for approaching food and establishing a healthy food mindset. This book is not a diet plan; however, it does contain a lot of practical tips and suggestions for healthy habit formation.

Still, I realize that each person's process will be a little different. Some of you will find success just by mirroring my experience, while others will want to use this book as a companion to another proven long-term weight program, like Weight Watchers. Regardless of how you choose to proceed, I encourage you to think past the traditional diet routine.

We can't predict what tomorrow holds, but I can promise you your tomorrow is fashioned by today's choices.

Today can be your day to start a new journey. You can recapture control over your body and your

> **Channel your thoughts about food into positive, meaningful change and allow God to focus your actions.**

life by surrendering your food struggle to God. But remember, lasting success will only come with lasting change. Instead of looking for another diet or another workout plan, it's time to alter your relationship with food for good by asking God to help reveal what you truly believe about the food you eat. Only then can He enable you to eat with awareness and establish eating habits to follow for the rest of your life.

I did it and, for the first time in my life, God helped take weight off its pedestal in my head. Now, I am living fully and freely in Him.

Your tomorrow is fashioned by today's choices.

Chapter 2

Developing A Weight Loss Mindset

IF YOU ARE ANYTHING LIKE me, then you have been lured into buying a magazine because the front cover offered the key to unlocking the secrets of weight loss. And likely, you've tried countless approaches to shedding the pounds.

Personally, I have done calorie counting, diabetic exchanges, low carbohydrates, frequent small meals and no sugar, to name a few. Admittedly, each diet method worked for a season. In fact, I can think of multiple diet scenarios that culminated with a big smile and a satisfactory number on the scale. However, as soon as the diet was "over" it was only a matter of time before my weight started creeping up once again.

The pay-for-progress mentality is an interesting one. Somewhere along the way, we buy into the idea that we can only get what we pay for or that something is only worth trying if it comes in a program or has a catchy title. While this is typically true for a lot of things, I no longer think this philosophy fosters life-long success with weight. Take a moment to make a list of the techniques or programs you have used when trying to lose weight.

Why didn't these programs bring lasting results? Because, they never really got to what makes you overeat in the first place: your head. What's more, most of these programs could not be incorporated seamlessly into your daily life. People who successfully manage their weight eventually come to the realization that successful weight maintenance never ends.

How to Finally Wrap Your Head Around Your Weight

People who
successfully
manage
their weight
eventually
come to the
realization
that successful
weight
maintenance
never ends.

When struggling with weight, we are consistently bombarded by our ever-increasing feelings of weakness and our seemingly decreasing sense of self-control. Inevitably, I had to come to terms with these emotions and feelings in the context of my faith.

Lack of Self-Control

In one of the New Testament's best known narratives, the Apostle Paul lists 9 essential character qualities for holy living, commonly referred to as the fruits of the Spirit: love, joy, peace, forbearance, kindness, goodness, faithfulness, gentleness, and self-control.[4]

I have often wondered why self-control was included in this list. The other character traits fall into place quite easily in my thinking, especially in regard to my relationships with others. But, the whole issue of self-control seemed to hit on a more personal level. This is probably because my struggle with weight always seemed to put me at odds with the issue of self-control, primarily because my life story with weight constantly reminded me of how out of control I was.

Now, some who know me would look at me and say, "Shellie, you have never struggled with weight like many others do." And this brings up an interesting point: Is the person who gains 100 to 200 extra pounds more out-of-control than the person who repeatedly goes through the difficult process to lose 25 to 30 pounds only to allow them to creep back again and again? I would answer that indeed both types of people are out of control!

Thinking back to all of my "successful" diet attempts, I would estimate that I have lost around 150 pounds in major multiple-month diets in my lifetime. This does not count the two-to-three week diets that are too numerous to count. This puts me in the category of the majority of overweight adults who carry an average of 20 extra pounds.

As a Christian, I had prayed numerous times for God to give me the strength to overcome my struggle with food. But I ultimately had to get to that point that I was willing to put some action behind my pleas, which is so often what God wants us to do in the first place.

Had I put action behind my prayers before? Yes, I had successfully navigated a host of different diet strategies that inevitably required a significant level of energy and dedication. But, these diets were always targeted for the short-term. Although I never realized it at the time, I never intended to maintain the same level of determination once I lost the weight. In fact, the self-control required to successfully navigate those diets was all but forgotten once I no longer saw a bigger me in the mirror.

Consider your own thinking about food, rather than just focus on the symptom of weight that results from eating too much of it.

So, in essence, I always got what I prayed for. I asked God to help me lose the weight and to give me determination to stick with my diet plans and that's what I got. Never had I considered asking for God's help to end my struggle with food for good.

I believe this critical distinction is what made this time so different. I wasn't looking to merely lose weight. Instead, the idea occurred to me that I should actually consider my own thinking about food, rather than just focus on the symptom of weight that results from eating too much of it.

Many times, what we attribute to our own creativity or intuitiveness is actually revelation. I had successfully navigated multiple diets in the past, but I had never once considered addressing my actual thoughts and mindset about food along the way, which proved to be the missing piece of the puzzle.

Target Faulty Thinking with Truth

Once I figured out what made me tick with food and my assumptions about food, then I could target some of my faulty thinking with truth. Jesus had a discourse with his disciples in which he discussed the concept of knowing the truth and following what we know to be true.

He said these words, "Then you will know the truth, and the truth will set you free." (John 8:32, NIV) When Jesus entered public ministry, he chose these 12 men to be part of his inner circle. He told them that they would learn to know the truth and that truth would set them free.

In John 8:32, Jesus proclaimed that he was the way and the truth. So, how did his disciples finally come to know him as the truth? They spent extensive time with him, they asked him questions, and they learned from his day-in-and-day-out example.

Eventually, the truth of Jesus became clear to them and they developed a keen sense of purpose and direction. That's why the Christian faith continues to thrive to this day.

So, what does this all have to do with our weight struggle? Each of us has a truth and a belief system that informs our relationship with food; however, that truth is yet unknown. If we consciously knew what made us click with food, if we understood exactly what propels us and causes us to feel so helpless to its draw, then we would do something about it!

That's why I believe this journey of self-discovery is so essential for uncovering our expectations, attitudes, and mental blocks with food. If we can spend an extended time period exploring and questioning our thoughts and actions with food, then we can establish sustainable habits and practices that will set us free to pursue lives where food does not have the final say.

Once I got a handle on the truth about food and my relationship and response to it, then I felt free to exercise more self-control. For the first time, I felt like I was in control of my relationship with food. More importantly, that inner struggle with food disappeared. You know what I'm talking about. It's that inner self-talk that goes on when your will and your mind are at odds with each other over a particular food choice.

Once you get a handle on the truth about food and your relationship and response to it, then you will be free to exercise more self-control.

You will probably recognize this scenario because it has played out in your own head. You tell yourself you will not eat any sweets today, then lo and behold, you arrive at work to find out it's your boss' birthday and he has treated the office to a donut feast. The self-talk begins, "I can't have a donut…They look so good.... You have got to stay strong.... Why is there always something tempting to eat?.... Maybe just half.... But that was so yummy.... Maybe one more bite, or the rest of this donut.... Ok, I have to stop.... But that was so good.... Maybe a bite more and then no lunch.... Ok, then half.... Might as well finish it.... Ok, now no lunch....(3 hours later after blood sugar has tanked).... I won't make it to the end of the day without lunch.... Man, I blew it AGAIN!"

Does this sound familiar? It's a scenario for failure and self-condemnation that I have cycled through hundreds of times. But finally, I developed a new framework of grace that took me from the position of victim to overcomer in my relationship with food.

I finally realized that it wasn't enough to change my habits for a few weeks or a few months to achieve my weight goals. Instead, I had to put on new habits and a new way of approaching food for a lifetime. "You were taught, with regard to your former way of life, to put off your old self, which is being corrupted by its deceitful desires; to be made new in the attitude of your minds; and to put on the new self, created to be like God in true righteousness and holiness." (Eph. 4:22-24, NIV)

If you are struggling with your weight, then you already know you've got a lot of habits that have got to go. Basically, you have become a slave to the same old habits and patterns with food. So, no matter how many times you have attempted to lose the weight in the past, you still end up right back in the same place.

It isn't enough to change your habits for a few weeks or a few months to achieve your weight goals. Instead, you have to put on new habits and a new way of approaching food for a lifetime.

Here's the thing: you can't just expect to remove a huge chunk of your daily choices and behaviors and then go on with life as usual. Instead, you've got to establish new eating habits and new behaviors with food to put in place of the old, ineffective habits that were ingrained in your old way of life.

If approached purposely, you can establish a new mindset and approach to food that makes sense for you. In fact, it will make so much sense that you won't ever need to resort to your old habits again.

Ok, so what do you say? Are you ready to put off those old habits that haven't served you at all? Are you ready to get to the bottom of your struggles with food? You are about to embark on a journey of self-discovery to determine what you really believe about food. You will uncover some interesting assumptions and some seriously flawed thinking over the next several weeks. But hopefully, you will gain some powerful insights to set the foundation for a new successful future with weight.

Journaling

Insanity has been defined as doing the same thing over and over again, while still expecting different results. Does this sound like your typical weight gain and weight loss scenario? Here's the thing: weight is only the outward symptom of your behavior with food. But, your behavior with food comes from your thinking about food.

Healthy mindsets with food are not forged by strict diets or short-term behavior modification. They are established for a lifetime. Essentially, if you really want to win over your weight, take the "finish line" out of your thinking.

I honestly believe that you can change your way of thinking, but you cannot expect to get rid of one mindset without putting a new one in its place. What will be your plan for overcoming your weight gain/loss cycle with food?

To *find my weigh*, I took a completely different approach from anything I had tried in the past. I decided to record my thoughts along the way through journaling. When it comes to journaling in terms of weight, most people think of calorie counting, which I have done on several past diets.

The traditional idea of food journaling involves writing down every morsel that goes into one's mouth in order to keep an accurate calorie count. Typical food journaling may also include the number of food group servings consumed. This type of journaling emphasizes the diet mentality because it focuses entirely on calorie restriction as a means for weight loss.

If you really want to win over your weight, take that "finish line " out of your thinking.

After years of yo-yo dieting, I finally got off the weight merry-go-round by setting a prolonged 50-day period to journal my thoughts about food as I took steps to break unhealthy habits and realign my portion expectations.

To uncover your thinking about food, you will write about your frustrations and small victories, noting when you feel the hungriest. Pay special attention to the foods you find especially difficult to resist. Most importantly, record your self-talk, the internal dialogue that bounces around in your head when you face temptation.

Take steps to break your unhealthy habits and realign your portion expectations.

When you've only ever framed the activity of eating in physical terms, it's natural that you've allowed your physical desires to call the shots. Consequently, your behavior is conditioned to respond to your senses alone; if it looks good or smells good, then the body says, "Eat it!" In Romans 12:2, we are told, "Do not conform any longer to the pattern of this world, but be transformed by the renewing of your mind. Then you will be able to test and approve what God's will is — his good, pleasing and perfect will." The discipline of daily writing helps reveal patterns that you have conformed to for years; habits that you were previously unaware of. Only after you have consciously acknowledged your behavior can you ask

God to help you transform your thinking and renew your mind when it comes to food.

Quite frankly, when I first started, I didn't know what to expect from this exercise, but I was fed up with my inability to manage my weight. I decided it was time to get to the bottom of it. Slowly, an epiphanic thought took shape in my head after the first week of journaling. Ah yes, I just said, "epiphanic!" Merriam-Webster Dictionary defines this as the adjective form of epiphany:

> epiphany : a moment in which you
> suddenly see or understand something in
> a new or very clear way

My weight gain was a symptom of some seriously flawed thinking about food. I finally realized that I had always felt powerless with food. Honestly, I truly believed that I was unable to resist food and its draw. In retrospect, others who so confidently choose the most sensible menu items or pass on the yummy desserts have always perplexed me. I guess I just figured that my willpower was either broken or misaligned.

However, the process of journaling helped pinpoint specific beliefs that caused me to make wrong food choices. In essence, I began to see how my actions with food were directly aligned with my expectations, beliefs, and food mindset. Basically I was acting on my beliefs.

Once you bring your behavior out into the light of day, God can then shine His truth on it. You've likely asked yourself, "Why did I eat that?" on more than one occasion. In fact, you'd admit that you've acted in ways that didn't even seem reasonable in retrospect. That's because your head wasn't in the game. Instead, you were acting purely on physical impulse.

Reading back through my journal entries, I can see that the light bulb turned on sometime around the end of the second week. God was literally transforming my thoughts through my writing. Until that point, my observations largely centered upon the physical sensations and behavioral modification that dieting requires. My thoughts all conformed to the typical way I had always acted and reacted to food. However, I eventually started to notice how essential my mind was to the whole process. Here is an excerpt from my journal entry:

Once you bring your behavior into the light of day God can then shine His truth on it.

Day 12

Alright, today I am back on track. It is becoming more and more clear to me that the true key to weight loss and management is in the mind. Of course, weight gain is caused by excess food; however, I am the one who ultimately makes the choice of what, when, and where I eat. I like this idea... I have a choice. If I overeat one day, I can choose to right things the next day without heaping on unwanted feelings of failure and discouragement. Just get back on track; finished and done.

Initially, my journaling was an experiment. I had no idea if journaling my thoughts about food would benefit me at all. Of course if I had known what a powerful impact it would have on my food habits, I would have done it a long time ago.

As I mentioned earlier, food is inextricably linked with who we are. It is an integral part of our cultural memories and emotions. If you can accept that premise then you should be able to take the next logical step.

How to Journal Your Thoughts about Food

Starting today, you will begin journaling your thoughts, expectations, and self-talk to *find your weigh* with food.

For the next 50 days, you will end each day by writing down your thoughts about food. There are no rules for your writing, except that your writing must center on the theme of food. Here are some ideas of various thought processes to consider.

Observations

Sights, sounds, and smells that triggered a reaction

- What foods were particularly hard to resist? Why?

- Would you be satisfied to have a few bites? Why or why not?

Actions you performed out of habit

- Do you waste a lot of calories on thoughtless foods or beverages? (ex. drinks)

- Do you eat without even thinking about the food? (ex. eating while working, eating in front of the television, eating in the car)

- Do you eat out of bags or bowls without considering the amount?

- Did you eat by the clock, instead of cues from your body?

- Did you eat to be social?

- Did you go straight to food out of anger, stress, or boredom?

- When approached with a large variety of foods, do you just dive in without a plan?

Frustrations

- Does exercising self-control make food feel less fun?

- How did exercising self-control make you feel?

- Did you feel unworthy of God's love and patience or did you feel impatient with yourself?

- What disappoints you?

Self-talk

- Record your inner dialogue...that battle that goes on in your head when you are considering eating "just one more piece," or "paying for it tomorrow."

- What goes on in your head when you are considering a snack?

- What thoughts come to mind when you see tempting food?

- Did you battle feelings of self-condemnation?

- Did you feel like your battle was more spiritual than physical?

Expectations

- Do you have expectations of your food? (ex. my food should entertain, comfort, or calm me?)

- Do you expect the temptation of food to be more than you can handle?

Assumptions

- Do you automatically assume you will overeat in certain situations? Why?

- Do you assume that certain foods must be served with calorie-laden sides?

- .Do you assume that you have to have a particularly calorie-laden food for a particular event or occasion?

- Do you assume that you can only be satisfied with a particular food if you eat lots of it?

This list is just a starting point, but it should give you an idea of the thought processes you need to target through your journaling. The 50-Day Journal begins at this point in the book for a couple of reasons:

1. Hopefully, you now have a better idea why you should even consider journaling to uncover your true thoughts about food.

2. I have explained why the traditional diet model is ineffective.

Starting today, begin your 50 days of journaling. The *Find Your Weigh* journal is located at the end of the book for easy reference.

How to Utilize the Scale

Do you have a love-hate relationship with the scale? Has the number on the scale ever brought tears to your eyes? It has to mine. Most of us are accustomed to using the scale to measure our weight. That is all fine and good as long as we stop there. However, the struggle comes when we allow the number that we see to determine how we feel about ourselves. This is the point where we chose helplessness over hopefulness.

I have definitely had my struggles with the scale and I have launched into a number of self-berating sessions, but ultimately it wasn't feelings of shame or helplessness that finally propelled me forward in my journey with weight.

First, let me say that I believe the scale is a great tool for keeping weight in check. In fact, I think it is the single most effective way to maintain a consistent weight because it is not influenced by our emotions or denial. The dial measures one thing: pounds.

Since settling into a comfortable weight for my height and lifestyle, I have utilized the scale on a daily basis to monitor my weight each morning before I eat any food. I allow myself a 5 pound range that runs 2 pounds below and 2 pounds above my body's set point. This range takes into account various metabolic changes, like water retention.

Consistent monitoring allows me to take immediate action when the weight starts to creep up. It's much easier to address a weight gain of one or two pounds rather than waiting until you've gained 10 pounds! Usually, a one or two pound gain can be remedied with a week of increased movement and by cutting down on sweets and carbohydrates.

3-Week Exception to Daily Weighing

How many times have you been compelled to weigh yourself and then wished that you hadn't? For me, the disappointment of seeing unsatisfactory numbers has been enough to derail some of my best weight loss efforts.

Despite its extreme value for weight maintenance, the scale can be immensely burdensome and emotionally deflating when you are first trying to lose weight. In the beginning, your weight can vary widely from day-to-day or even hour-to-hour.

So, what does extreme fluctuation mean for weight loss? I noticed an interesting trend in my last few unsuccessful diet attempts. I would take a few deep breaths and make a game plan. Then, after a few days of deprivation and headaches from sugar withdrawal, I would stand on the scale to find no change. In fact, at times the number actually increased!

Now, I'm not new to the weight loss routine. I am quite aware of the physical demands of the first weeks; however, I used to get reassurance from the scale after the first few days. So, a downward movement on the dial would really give me the push I needed to continue on. However, this is not always the case at different stages of our lives. Consequently, valiant attempts to establish new eating habits can crash and burn largely because of the scale.

For years, I had grown accustomed to the consistent reassurance of the scale to propel me along. But, the realities of fluctuating water weight can make numerical weight loss almost imperceptible in the first weeks. You see, the scale only measures your actual weight at any given moment; it is not intuitive. It doesn't take hormones into account, nor does it distinguish the extra weight of new muscle. It doesn't know that you are retaining water because you took in a little too much sodium.

Consequently, the real possibility exists that you can stand on the scale at the end of a long week only to feel deflated and defeated by the number staring back at you. I can count three separate attempts in the year prior to my breakthrough that were derailed after a week or two when the pointer just refused to budge.

Our relationship with the scale can be a love-hate one. We want to pick it up and kiss it when we are doing well and we all can say a few things about what we want to do with it when the number is less than pleasing! Unfortunately I, like many of you, have looked to that simple contraption for validation. Let me say this loud and clear, the scale can only register your weight. It does not display your integrity, confidence, or self-worth. Only you can do that. How?...by remembering that God's opinion of you is the only one that counts. He goes to great links to convince you of your value as His child throughout the pages of scripture.

God's opinion of you is the only one that counts!

I have come to the conclusion that constantly stepping on the scale in the initial stages of weight loss can be counterproductive. This time, try to avoid the scale for the first 3 weeks.

I got the idea to avoid the scale from several articles I read on the Paleo diet. While I didn't agree with all aspects of that approach, I did like their suggestion that the scale fails to provide the best feedback for determining success in weight loss or management.

Now, to a girl who has always lived and died by the scale, this was a revolutionary concept, so I settled on the three-week mark for banning the scale. Does this sound impossible to you? I did it and it really helped jumpstart my weight loss efforts.

It's Time to Start Moving

You knew this was coming or you should have. Food is only one part of the equation, albeit a very large part. But there is one last piece that still needs to find its way into your life. If you want lasting success with weight...exercise.

Credible research confirms that food consumption is the number one consideration in weight management, because our bodies basically process food calories for energy: 3,500 calories equal one pound. Each person's body burns a specified amount of calories each day to function. Therefore, once the person consumes the number of calories his body needs in a day, the rest are either burned off through physical activity or stored as fat.

Wow, that all sounds so simple; however, the reality is not quite so cut and dry. While it's true that each person's body burns a certain amount of calories,

The scale can only register your weight. It does not display your integrity, confidence, or self-worth. Only you can do that!

that amount depends largely on how much fat a person carries and how active she is.

While this whole scenario is not particularly simple, I want to make sure you make one important observation. You must get your food consumption in check to have lasting success over weight. Increasing your fitness level will help you accomplish this in two important ways:

Exercising for a sustained period of time burns calories.

This allows for a greater calorie deficit when you are actively losing weight. Then, once you settle in at a comfortable weight, you can eat a little more in a normal day because the extra calories will be burned off through exercise.

Weight training and weight bearing exercises build muscle.

Muscle tissue burns more calories at rest than fat tissue, which means the greater your percentage of lean muscle tissue, the more calories your body will burn at rest.

Exercise

So, you've tried to convince yourself that you don't have time for exercise.

You must get your food consumption in check to have lasting success over weight.

This is an easy conclusion to come by considering the hectic schedules many of us keep; juggling our work and family obligations. Actually, people didn't use to have to plan their exercise. Their daily lives were full of exertion and movement. Now, our lives have become so convenient that we hardly have to get up from our chairs except to eat and go to the bathroom. Exercise has become something you do, something you have to plan for, or in many cases, something you ignore. Along with the time element, we should also add the sensationalized perception that gyms are full of only super-fit people wearing cute workout outfits.

Webster defines exercise as, "physical activity that is done in order to become stronger and healthier."

Wow, that really simplifies the whole issue, doesn't it? It does not say anything about wearing spandex or joining any special programs. It boils down to engaging in any activity that will promote your health and make you stronger.

I want to challenge you to add movin' it to your current perception of exercise. Movin' it just means adding movement to your days. I have traditional exercise days and I have movin' it days. On my designated "exercise days," I actually go to the gym for group classes. But, that doesn't mean that I stop there. The other days I focus on movin' it, which usually means adding spurts of walking throughout my day.

Remember that steps are steps, so you can increase your movement by adding another lap from the living room, through the kitchen, down the hallway and back at the top of each hour or every time you get up from your chair. I bought a pedometer that measures my steps. It is amazing how much additional exercise you can fit into the day if you focus on making small, thoughtful changes to your routine.

Fitting Exercises into Your Day

There are only so many hours in the day. So, it can be really frustrating to consider losing weight or getting fit when you can't see where it will fit into your busy day. While it is possible, it is a scenario that requires some extra planning.

Today, I'm movin' it!

Have you found yourself asking the question, "How can I lose weight when I sit all day?" Here are some practical tips for adding movement to your work days and focusing your weight loss efforts.

Practical Step
Move It Throughout The Day

- Is your building multi-storied? If so, take the stairs.

- Park further from the building.

- Walk at least 10 minutes of your lunch break.

- If possible, buy an exercise ball to sit on instead of a chair for at least a portion of the day. Doing this requires you use muscle control to maintain your balance.

- Lift your legs off the floor and hold them for periods of time. This will work your stomach muscles.

Practical Step

Plan a Weight Loss Competition

Everything is better when done with a friend and that includes weight loss. Consider organizing a weight loss competition with some of your co-workers. There are a lot of free materials available on the internet to organize a competition at the work place.

I have organized two competitions in the past and they were both hugely successful. One tip is to have winners in two categories: weight lost and inches lost. This helps to level the playing field and also encourages participants to engage in physical activity and fitness instead of concentrating solely on food and calorie restriction.

A friendly competition can be very motivating, not to mention it makes it super easy to find someone to walk with at lunch or after work!

Goal : Practical Step:
Exercise at Least 20 Minutes

You are much more likely to fit your exercise in if you do it immediately after you return home from work before other chores and responsibilities start vying for your attention.

Remember, a journey always starts with a step!

Chapter 3

Assess Your Expectations

IF ASKED, MOST OF US could immediately come up with a number—that number that represents the time we felt the best about our weight. It is that ideal weight when we felt we were at our best. I bet you can picture it now: there you are in your cheerleading uniform or wedding dress flashing your most dazzling smile. Now, you look back at those pictures and wonder, "Where did that girl go?"

It seems as if the years have dragged you, kicking and screaming, to a place you don't want to be. You look down at the scale and see an all-too-real number that does not even slightly resemble that number you carry around in your head. Here we have the ideal versus real dilemma.

Ideal vs Real

Here is an important thing to acknowledge about that perfect picture of yourself you have firmly tucked in your head...most likely, the "perfect you" was younger than the person reading these words today. Change has occurred with each passing year. You may have faced multiple stresses or undergone various medical procedures. For the women out there, you may have birthed several kids, not to mention the hormonal changes that come with age.

It's helpful to realign your weight expectations to match the body you have here and now. Keep in mind that body composition changes with age. Typically, our body fat percentage increases as we get older.

Healthy body fat percentages for men range from 8-20% (age 20-39 yrs) and 11-22% (age 40-59 yrs). For women, healthy body fat percentages range from 21-33% (age 20-39 yrs) and between 23-34% (age 40-59 yrs).[5]

Instead of focusing on an ideal weight, you can achieve a significant metabolism boost by losing 7 to 10% of your current body weight. Then, you can reevaluate your situation at that point. Once you have established a weight loss mindset and healthier habits to reach your first goal, it becomes easier to set a new one. Remember, the "ideal" is only a number that does not necessarily reflect your current life or circumstances.

The "real" you has climbed some mountains and has stories to tell. Undoubtedly, you may have stumbled along the way, but scars are a reminder that you have lived. When we idealize our younger, fitter selves, we can focus so much on physical appearance that we forget the miles we've traveled to get where we are. This does not mean that you should not desire to improve yourself; however, it does mean you should make an honest evaluation without the rose-colored glasses.

What Are God's Expectations?

Here, we find ourselves once again at a point of decision. Is our struggle physical, emotional, or spiritual? By now you should be figuring out that it's all of these. Our expectations are informed by numerous internal and external factors.

We would be fooling ourselves to say that our physical appearance has nothing to do with this endeavor. When God sent the prophet Samuel out to anoint the future king of Israel, Samuel naturally assumed that one of Jesse's older sons was God's choice. They were strong, good-looking men who ticked all of the expected boxes in terms of appearance and ability. But God reminded him in 1 Samuel 16:7, "The Lord does not look at the things man looks at. Man looks at outward appearance, but the Lord looks at the heart."

God doesn't regard your size as a measure of your worth or value. It's ok to pursue a goal of becoming leaner and more fit as long as you understand that your weight does not qualify or disqualify you in God's eyes. Ultimately, the goal needs to be a heart goal…God change me from the inside out!

Aligning Our Expectations with the Right Reality

At one time or another, we have all daydreamed about some unattainable item or situation. Unfortunately, many people give up on weight loss as a reachable goal and relegate it to the realm of dreams or wishful thinking because they establish such unrealistic expectations.

Sports cars are often big "wish list" items. For the sake of illustration, I want you to visualize a sports car. The sleek structure of a sports car bears a striking resemblance to the body of a fitness model: clean lines without bumps and bulges.

The essential problem with wish lists is that they seldom come with an action plan.

I did a little research on a sports car. The 918 Porsche Spyder costs $845,000.00 plus a $2,975.00 delivery fee.[6] At 6%, the sales tax would be $50,878.50. This brings the total to $898,853.50. According to CNN Money, the average American household had a median income of $53,657.00 in 2014.[7] This means the average person can rest in the knowledge that he or she can almost afford the sales tax.

In the end, the reality of you parking that Porsche in your garage is pretty much nil to none. Now, compare this scenario to your weight loss aspirations. Is weight loss on your wish list? The essential problem with wish lists is that they seldom come with an action plan. Do you have realistic expectations for your weight loss? Are your weight loss goals realistically attainable or are they more in the realm of a shiny sports car in your garage?

Just like the dream of an uber-expensive sportscar, our expectations and dreams of weight loss can become so unrealistic that we unconsciously shelve them away on a wish list of impossibilities.

Evaluate Your Expectations

To what level are you willing to abstain from certain foods for the physical trade-off? How much are you really willing to invest in your ideal body and keep investing to keep it? Are you setting realistic goals that keep fitness and food in balance with the other areas God has called you to pursue? The fitness models in most of the inspiration pictures you have pinned have made significant trade-offs. Here is the typical body composition of a fitness model:

The body fat percentage rate for fitness models is low compared to a normal or healthy range of body fat. According to the American Council of Exercise, it falls slightly above the range of "essential fat" necessary for bodily functions, which is 10 to 13 percent for women and 2 to 5 percent for men. A fitness model's low body fat can eventually affect the healthy functions of the body, including a woman's reproductive functions.

To maintain this body type, fitness models maintain a daily regimen of exercise, diet, and nutrition supplements. Many practice "extreme" weight-loss methods, such as water restriction, crash dieting, and purging as they prepare for an upcoming shoot or appearance. These practices are inherently unhealthy and should not be an example of how to lose weight or maintain a fit and healthy body weight.[8]

Those rock-hard abs and chiseled physiques are forged by hours of exercise and strictly maintained diets. Except in rare cases of extremely good genetics, people who achieve those types of results have made conscious decisions to give up large categories of foods in exchange for peak physical results.

Are you that type of person? Are you realistically willing to place certain foods off-limits for the rest of your life to attain these types of results?

If you cannot picture yourself making drastic changes to your diet for the long haul, then it's time to reevaluate your expectations. Consistently ask yourself if your dreams for a smaller you line up with God's good and perfect plan for your life. God alone is the giver and sustainer of your life and He ultimately wants what's best for you, so it makes sense to trust Him with your weight dreams.

Consider making changes you can actually sustain, then entrust those dreams to God who knows you better than anyone else. Would you still be satisfied with a trimmer, healthier version of yourself even if you didn't end up looking like a fitness model? If you would, then consider culling out some of those "motivational" media images that may actually be harming your efforts instead of helping them.

Instead, keep God front and center in this process. His plans for you are good and full of grace. He will speak truth into your dreams, which ultimately form the foundation of your expectations. In John 16:13, Jesus promises that the Holy Spirit will "guide you into all truth. He will not speak on his own; he will speak only what he hears, and he will tell you what is yet to come."

Chapter 4

Change The Diet Mentality

Stop Saying the "D" Word

WHEN PEOPLE THINK OF LOSING or maintaining weight, they immediately think... diet. How many times have you summoned up all possible willpower to launch into a diet, meticulously counted every bite that went into your mouth for a week or two, lost a few pounds, and then gained it back by the next week? I have been there and done that more times than I can count. We want the results, and we want our weight to be a quick-fix situation, but unfortunately our bodies just don't work that way.

Diets are short-term behavioral modifications designed to lower body weight. But, the weight is only a symptom of one's eating habits. So, no matter how hard a person works to target the weight, the habits that caused the weight to mount in the first place remains untouched, just waiting to emerge again. Short-term diets can never yield a long-term mentality.

In terms of developing a long-term weight mentality, I thought we could take a stroll through the pages of history for an object lesson. The Titanic sank on its maiden voyage, largely because the financial backers of the ocean liner were in a rush to launch their masterpiece of engineering before a rival company could launch its own ocean liner.

In their book *What Really Sank The Titanic*, the metal experts contend that the vessel's manufacturer was under great pressure to secure enough iron to make three million rivets to stitch the ship's metal plates. In the rush to beat competition from Cunard, the White Star liner was constructed with substandard materials.[9]

Weight is only a symptom of a person's eating habits.

So, why did I decide to dig into the historical archives to pull out this story? This example illustrates that rushing often does not yield the most desirable results and in fact it can be disastrous. Yes, the Titanic looked great for a few days, but in the end, the rush to launch ended up with a huge ocean liner at the bottom of the ocean. A diet, or rush mentality, may get you a few "wow, you've lost weight!" comments, but will it set you on a path to put your weight under control once and for all?

Diets Condition You to Expect Hunger and Deprivation

Do you typically expect losing weight to be painful or a test of endurance? I can definitely say that I have never anticipated a diet. None of us want to envision a life of discomfort or dissatisfaction. But, when we grow accustomed to associating these feelings with managing our weight, we unknowingly set up an unsustainable pattern. Basically, we adopt short-term, endurance thinking, rather than instituting sustainable life-long habits.

You may have tried to convince yourself that hunger and headaches are necessary penance for dropping the pounds. So, when your stomach starts growling in the mid-afternoon and you feel that growing ache in the back of your head, you assume you have to grin and bear it if you really want to lose the weight. However, instead of grinning, you are more likely to blurt out something unfortunate to whomever happens to be in earshot at the time. The truth is, the longer you ignore your body's signals, the more you want to dive into a bag of chips as soon as you hit the front door, or worse, you end up "taste testing" a whole dinner serving before the evening meal even hits the table.

Rushing does not yield the most desirable results and at times it can be disastrous.

Using Hunger to Control Weight Always Backfires

Hunger is not healthy or sustainable. Here I am referring to two distinct, yet equally motivating forms of hunger. There's physiological hunger, which represents your body's need for nutrients, but there is an equally motivating hunger, which is an emotional yearning for food.

When we grow accustomed to associating hunger with managing our weight, we unknowingly set up an unsustainable pattern.

We've all experienced that emotional yearning; you never know how much hunger you possess for a particular food item until you tell yourself you are no longer permitted to eat it under any circumstances.

I Eliminated the "D" Word

I eliminated the "D" word from the first day of my successful weight journey. No longer was I going to chain myself to a futile practice that had failed me over and over in the past. Instead, I began telling my friends and family I was making a lifestyle change.

It finally sank in...the only way to change my relationship with food was to change my food habits forever. No short-term diet solution was ever going to yield long-term results. I had 25 years of experience to back this up.

What's more, I consciously chose to start my lifestyle change without setting a goal weight. What? No goal weight?! Don't get me wrong, goal-setting has extreme value for many things in the realm of health and fitness. However, in the diet culture, weight goals are always associated with a finish line: that point when all your hard work pays off and the deprivation ends.

How many times have you rewarded yourself for reaching your goal weight by over-indulging in food? Stop right here and take the time to count. How many weight goals have you reached in your life? Write that number here: _6_. Did reaching your weight goals ever lead to lasting change? My guess is "no," otherwise you wouldn't be reading this book.

This time, consider setting a life goal. I know this may all sound a little too cerebral right now, but that's exactly the point. Your thoughts determine your actions, so you've got to start telling yourself something different if you want to have different results than you've ever had before.

> The only way you are ever going to change your relationship with food is to change your food habits forever.

What Kinds of Food Should I Eat?

There are so many opinions out there about food. I wouldn't doubt that there is some group out there who proposes that we all just sit around and think about food, rather than actually eat "anything"! Hmmm, the whole thing is enough to make a girl's head spin.

I think food is a great thing! As I mentioned earlier in this book, food binds cultures together; it also symbolizes family, memories, traditions, and God's abundant blessings. So maybe we are so conflicted about food because we can't seem to wade through all the mixed messages: Is food good or bad? Should I embrace it or shun it?

In order to develop healthy food habits, it's important to embrace food as the immense blessing it is, but in a balanced way. God created food to nourish us, enrich us, and bless us. In fact, God's provision of food actually speaks to His character as a loving God who provides for His children.

If food really is a blessing, then it makes sense to eat foods in the forms that are closest to the way they are found in nature. Yes, God did create the potato, but you are never going to dig up a potato that's deep-fried or hidden under a mound of melted cheese, sour cream, and bacon bits.

I believe "clean" eating is a good way to start. Oh wow, so here I go throwing out a confusing term! So, what is clean eating anyway? Frankly, I thought I had it figured out, but then I keep seeing the term used in conflicting ways.

For our purposes, clean eating means consuming foods that are made out of component ingredients that can be readily identified. I did a little research to see if I was totally off-base or if there is actually an explanation that jives with my own interpretation. I came across this article on the ABC News website:

> The truth is, it's a very simple concept. "In some ways, clean eating is what eating was always about," said Dr. David Katz, director of the Yale University Prevention Research Center.

> *"Food that's clean is food that's for the most part real food and not encumbered with things that compromise health: artificial flavorings, artificial colorings, sugar substitutes," said Katz. The clean eating rule of thumb: The shorter the ingredient list, the better. No specific food is off-limits as long as it's a real, honest-to-goodness food. In other words, this isn't a "diet" that bans bread or sacrifices sugar. "I don't think sugar makes food unclean. Pure fruits are not unclean foods. You can add sugar to foods, and it can be clean.... It's not about banishing any particular type of ingredient," said Katz. "It needs to be a holistic concept. There's a real danger in placing it on just one ingredient."[10]*

Why Should You Consider Eating Clean?

I am sure you have heard the saying, "You are what you eat." Well, that is exactly what medical health professionals are telling us. Our immune, digestive, and metabolic systems are all affected by the foods we eat. Food choice also directly affects how our brains function, which naturally extends to the whole body.

Processed foods are cheap to produce, have a long shelf life, and are easy to store and distribute. Most foods that have a long shelf life have to be colorized to keep them looking fresh. They also have to be combined with various preservatives to stop them from degrading. This does not mean that you can never buy foods that are processed or convenient, but rather, you have to be diligent in reading the ingredients labels to fully understand what you are purchasing. The ingredient label is just as important, if not more so, than the level of calories, fat grams, etc. that is displayed above it.[11]

Some Ingredients to Consider Cutting Out for Regular Consumption

Rather than placing all foods off-limits, maybe it's better to consider cutting out some of those food additives that are the most harmful to our bodies.

High-Fructose Corn Syrup

The body interprets high fructose corn syrup similarly to table sugar. Like sugar, this syrup contributes to weight gain, type 2 diabetes, and high triglyceride levels. However, more significant is the fact that we know when we've taken a bite out of a cupcake; however, we may not even be aware of how much of this sugar source we consume in processed foods.

Artificial Sweeteners

Unless you have been hiding under a rock for the last decade, you have heard something about the harmful effects of artificial sweeteners. Plainly put, they come with a laundry list of side effects. Again, I am not saying that I never drink a Coke Zero, but it is not a part of my steady diet.

Partially Hydrogenated Oils

These oils are chemically processed as solids to extend their shelf life. The bottom line on these oils is that your body is unable to break them down effectively, so a portion of the oil just hangs around and eventually sticks to the lining of your arteries. Go for the real stuff, like olive oil and real butter instead.

Artificial Dyes And Colors

Need I say more than they are artificial? There is significant study to suggest a correlation between different artificial components and a host of possible illnesses; including headaches, hyperactivity, and cancer, to name a few.

Clean eating is not about diets, eating fat-free, or banning all sugar. It really boils down to knowing what you are eating.

Practical Step

Think about the last thing you ate today. If asked, could you write down a list of the basic components of that food? If so, then I think you are on the right track toward clean eating.

I purposely did not add sugar to the list because I do not want to promote the idea that you can never enjoy dessert. Instead, consider how you can take a more moderate approach to consuming it.

Essentially, clean eating is majoring on the foods that you can see, pronounce, and define. For the most part, this idea takes one-step, processed entrees off the table. That doesn't mean that you will never eat processed mac and cheese again, but it does mean that you can serve it with other foods that have a simpler ingredients list. In the end, it's all about balance and moderation.

Chapter 5

Mental Blocks To Success With Weight

I'VE UNCOVERED THREE MENTAL BLOCKS that I now realize kept me in a constant cycle of weight gain and loss for decades. Essentially, I would start a diet to regain control of my eating only to hit one or all of these blocks, which would eventually send me right back to where I started.

As you journal, you will start recognizing some or all of these mental blocks in your own thinking about food. As you read through these different sections, think about how these blocks play out in your own relationship with food. You may also want to address them specifically during your journaling sessions.

I believe these three mental blocks are the greatest hindrances to progress along the weight journey.

1. Learned Helplessness
2. Short-Term Mentality
3. Fuel vs. Entertainment Dilemma

As I've mentioned already, our actions are rooted in our thinking. If your mind assumes you cannot resist a particular food or situation, you will typically act out your feelings of helplessness towards an inevitable outcome...you will not even try to resist.

Mental Block: Learned Helplessness

As a yo-yo dieter with well over 20 diets under my belt, I had developed an attitude of helplessness to food.

Adolescence is a time when you begin constructing the foundation for the adult version of you. However, my adolescence was characterized by looking and feeling different from most of my peers. I was short and chubby when most of them had to think very little about their weight and there was really little I could do about it, except wait it out until I grew several inches in height.

As an adult, I would not necessarily categorize myself as an undisciplined person. After all, there was a threshold that I refused to cross with my weight; however, I didn't seem to know how to keep the weight off once I lost it. In essence, I felt helpless to the draw of food, nor could I conceptualize a lifestyle scenario where moderation with food was even possible. For me, food seemed to be an all or nothing proposition and I accepted the weight loss/gain cycle as normal.

The idea of learned helplessness is a psychological term that refers to a person's unshakable mindset that she has no control over a particular situation. As a result, she gives up trying because she figures it's no use or that she is destined to behave a certain way.

God's word assures that we are indeed in a war against our own minds that tell us we're helpless based on what we've learned from our previous life experiences. Paul explained his inner struggle this way, "I find this law at work: When I want to do good, evil is right there with me. For in my inner being I delight in God's law; but I see another law at work in the members of my body, waging war against the law of my mind and making me a prisoner of the law of sin at work within my members." (Romans 7:21-23, NIV)

When a person wants to wage war against other addictive substances, like alcohol or drugs, she can just choose not to be around them anymore. All traces can literally vanish with a willful decision. But, this doesn't work with food because we have to eat to live.

We can never control every situation where food is served. While this is a hard reality to swallow, God is in the business of speaking hope into life's harshest realities. Yes, we're in a battle, but we are definitely not expected to fight it alone.

We live in constant tension between the pull of our body's willful desires and God's call to draw near to Him. The battle of our minds determines which way we lean in this weight struggle. Paul goes on to explain how this inner tug-of-war works, "Those who live according to the sinful nature have their minds set on what that nature desires; but those who live in accordance with the

Spirit have their minds set on what the Spirit desires… life and peace." (Romans 8:5 - 6b, NIV)

I am a self-confessed carb junkie. I love breads and potatoes, oh, and don't get me started on sweets. Undoubtedly, years of yo-yoing had convinced me that I could not resist the draw of carbs outside the confines of a self-imposed diet with a clearly defined endpoint. Really, it was an unspoken conviction that any success I might have with dieting was only temporary.

We're in a battle, but we are definitely not expected to fight it alone.

So, what did that mean for me? My eating habits would eventually revert back to the old and familiar after a diet because I thought I was helpless to do anything else. Of course, this is not true. Many people actually live their whole lives without struggling with their weight. So obviously, the trouble was with me.

Addressing the Pattern of Learned Helplessness

The real crux of the issue boils down to addressing your flawed thinking; that you will inevitably revert back to your old habits and be incapable of moderating your favorite foods in the future. Now, your previous experience provides ample evidence to support this fact and if you leave it to your own devices, you will likely fail just like you have in the past. However, you are no longer going to face this struggle as a physical issue to overcome in your own strength, but as a spiritual battle of the mind. Now, you've got something to rally your efforts because God promises He will, "give life to your mortal bodies through his Spirit, who lives in you." (Romans 8:11b, NIV)

This time, try resisting the mindset of learned helplessness with weight by implementing these steps:

1. Practice eating in moderation.

Honestly, I feel moderation gets an undeserved bad rap with a lot of people. It sounds so middle-of-the-road, doesn't it? I think that's because we have been conditioned to think that dieting is a natural part of the human experience. The common mindset is to expect to eat, and eat a lot, during certain situations; like special occasions, vacations, holidays or anytime a buffet is involved.

Practical Step

Do not count calories or fat grams. Instead, cut down your existing food amounts by half. At first, don't even try to change the types of food you are eating. Just the amount of those foods.

2. Allow yourself a few bites of any food you crave.

Just like a great idea will roll over and over in your mind, so will a food craving if it's not satisfied. Humans don't deal well with deprivation. Deprivation is perceived as a negative sensation. So, by choosing to deprive yourself of a particular food, you attach a negative feeling or emotion to that food. Therefore, to seek balance, your mind will obsess over that food item in an effort to "right the wrong" and make everything OK again.

Practical Step

When you have an unshakeable craving for a particular food, allow yourself to have a few bites of it. But first, make sure to separate out the amount you will eat before one bite goes into your mouth.

3. Do not count all eating as equal.

We eat for a multitude of reasons, only one of which is to fuel our bodies. Food is also used to commemorate, celebrate, and bond with other people. Because of this, you cannot count all eating equal. Learn to differentiate when food is part of the entertainment and when it is just a normal event.

Practical Step

When dining out or eating with friends, give yourself grace to eat a little more than you would at a typical meal. However, when eating a normal meal for fuel, consciously consider the amount of food you put on your plate.

4. Do not allow yourself to experience serious hunger pains.

Hunger does not help us develop a healthy relationship with food. The hungrier you allow yourself to become, the more helpless you feel to its draw.

Practical Step

Before you eat, take a moment to ask yourself, "Am I actually hungry or am I bored?"

5. Do not call it a diet.

Healthy thinking with food is established for a lifetime. You don't need to have a "finish line" in mind.

Practical Step

Do not use the "D" word from this day forward. You will feel compelled to tell others that you are trying to get your weight under control, so from now on, call your efforts what they are... a lifestyle change.

Mental Block: Short-Term Mentality

Short-term mentality is a modern-day phenomenon. We don't want to wait for anything and, for the most part, we don't have to. But with weight, as other things that are still organic elements of the natural world, there is not a quick-fix technological advancement, short of liposuction, that can go in and pull the fat out for us. But unfortunately, that does not mean that people aren't still searching for it. Still, many of us have a "getter' done" expectation when it comes to our weight.

I ran a search of the top Google key search terms for weight loss, and this is what I found:

1. weight loss

2. weight loss diet

3. weight loss program

4. weight loss pills

5. weight loss fast

6. weight loss and

7. weight loss surgery

8. weight loss quick

As you can see, searches for a quick-fix ranked 5th, 7th and 8th in terms of the most searched terms on Google. Interestingly enough, healthy weight loss ranked number 19.

We've all done it; we have a wedding or reunion on the horizon that we desperately want to look smashing for, so we launch an all-out attack of excruciating deprivation to hopefully appear somewhat smaller on the big day. The short-term mentality with weight is based on two faulty premises: that dieting is the essential, best process for losing weight, and that one can successfully lose weight overnight and actually keep it off. Let's break these down a bit.

The Two Faulty Assumptions of the Short-Term Mentality with Weight

Faulty Assumption 1: Dieting is the essential, best process for weight loss.

Actually, the term "diet" first surfaced around the 14th century to describe the bread and water regimen given to prisoners. The term became more widespread in the 19th century when food became more plentiful. Historically, up to that point, people spent most of their time and energy just trying to get enough food.

Dieting, at its core, is based on the idea of deprivation and self-denial. It is not something that most human beings can sustain for the long-term. What's more, it attaches a negative concept to food by labeling and categorizing it as good or bad. Since quick results can only be accomplished through strict dieting, the short-term mentality is detrimental to long-term, sustainable success with weight.

Faulty Assumption 2: You can actually keep weight off after you lose it quickly.

Dieting attaches a negative concept to food by labeling and categorizing it as good or bad.

A lot of research has been done on weight loss and the effects of dieting. Numerous studies confirm that short-term fixes don't work, primarily because the process of serious calorie restriction actually damages the body's metabolic process. We basically screw everything up when we try to deny our bodies the fuel they need to run properly. Although, we typically attribute our rapid re-expansion to falling off the wagon, there is often a lot more going on there than meets the eye.

Why Should You Ditch Your Short-Term Mentality with Weight?

According to the Centers for Disease Control, two out of three American adults are either overweight or obese.[12] WebMD places the average American at 23 pounds over his or her ideal body weight.[13]

If the recommended rate of safe weight loss is one-to-two pounds per week, we can then assume that a person who wants to take a healthy weight loss approach should expect to take a minimum of twelve weeks to reach his/her weight loss goals.

Practical Step

Now, it's time to look at your weight loss goals. Calculate how long it should realistically take you to lose your excess weight based on a conservative weight loss estimate of 1.5 pounds per week.

This period of time can be extremely helpful and motivating if viewed correctly. If you set out on your weight journey expecting it to take as long as it takes, the stress level and compulsion for results is greatly lessened. But even more importantly, an extended period of time provides the golden opportunity to get your head in the game and assess your assumptions, habits, and expectations about food. Instead of focusing on a goal weight, you can ditch the short-term mentality with weight by setting a goal to develop healthy thinking and a positive attitude about food for the long haul.

Mental Block: Entertainment vs Fuel Dilemma

Uncovering this mental block has been the single most helpful piece to the weight puzzle for me. There is nothing wrong with deriving enjoyment from food; however, problems arise when you expect your food to entertain you each and every time you eat. Inevitably, this expectation sent me running for food every time I got bored. It also caused me to consistently gravitate toward foods that appealed to the pleasure centers of my brain.

Obviously, food meets an essential human need that cannot be separated from our life equation. So, when did we start expecting our food to entertain us and stimulate us in addition to satisfying our hunger?

Food Becomes a Source of Entertainment

The idea of attaching entertainment to food is likely linked to the practice of eating out. Historically, dining out was a privilege reserved for only the richest and most elite levels of society. However, over the years, eating out has become commonplace in the lives of many. Here is an anthropologist's take on this mind shift:

> "If the rituals of eating out have become less grand for the mass of people, it still retains its aura as an "event."...We spend not so much for the food as for the entertainment value and the naughty thrill of being (we hope) treated like royalty in an otherwise drab democratic environment. Even lesser expeditions still have the air of

an event. The family outing to the local burger joint still has an air of preparation and difference; it can still be used to coax youngsters to eat, and provide a mild enough air of difference from routine to be "restorative." Even the necessary lunch for workers who cannot eat at home has been made into a ritual event by the relatively affluent among them.[14]

Couple this with the statistic from the United States Healthful Food Council that claims the average American adult buys a meal or snack from a restaurant almost six times per week.[15] This helps shed some light on how we have grown accustomed to viewing eating as an event. Now, add the overwhelming variety of foods that can be purchased at any grocery store and it's not surprising to see why we have grown to expect a certain wow-factor from our food.

Solving the Fuel vs Entertainment Dilemma with Foods

I can easily see where I fell into the trap of expecting my food to entertain me. For instance, if I ate a sandwich then I, of course, needed to add some chips to make the meal more interesting. When I went out to eat, I couldn't conceive of ordering a salad when I could have a burger and fries instead.

Now, I have developed a new thought process with my eating. Before a meal, I ask myself, "Is this for fuel or entertainment?" If the answer is fuel, then I stick to the basics, which means making food choices that satisfy my hunger without adding a lot of excess fat or calories.

However, if I am out with family or friends and the answer is entertainment, then I allow myself extended grace to eat richer options (still keeping portion size in mind) and enjoy the event. This renewed thinking puts me in the driver's seat with my food choices. More importantly, it prevents me from labeling foods as good and bad. Instead, particular foods are either well suited or not well suited for a particular situation.

Before a meal, ask yourself, "Is this for fuel or entertainment?"

It's one thing to take control of your home eating environment, but it's a whole other thing to try to order the seemingly endless stream of circumstances when you cannot choose the foods you are offered. Unfortunately, none of us can cocoon ourselves away from all food temptations, because food and life go hand-in-hand.

Jesus actually gave us some workable criteria for making our food choices in these types of situations. The Pharisees asked him to tell them the greatest commandments in the law and he answered, "Love the Lord your God with all your heart and with all your soul and with all your mind. This is the first and greatest commandment. And the second is like it: 'Love your neighbor as yourself.'" (Matthew 22:37 – 39, NIV)

You have to mentally prepare yourself for those occasions where you must navigate food in an entertainment setting. If someone invites you to an event or offers you food for a special occasion, feel free to eat it as a way of showing love for your neighbor. But also, take a moment to ask yourself, "How can I best glorify God in this situation?"

In this case, the question is not so much what you will eat, but how much of it. Paul addressed the issue of food in his first letter to the Corinthians. The Corinthian Christians were trying to figure out how to deal with social eating situations in which they did not control the menu. He reminded them, "'Everything is permissible' – but not everything is beneficial. 'Everything is permissible' – but not everything is constructive." (1 Corinthians 10:23, NIV)

While all food is literally on the table for you to eat, that does not mean that eating anything and everything is good for you physically or spiritually, nor is it necessary in an entertainment setting.

Fuel vs Entertainment Mental Checklist

1. Am I alone?

Typically, meals eaten alone should be for fuel. This is an important designation because people who overeat often do so in private. On these occasions, it is important to consider nutrition in your food choices.

2. Is the meal part of my normal routine?

Nightly family meals are a part of your normal routine, so they are fueling times. This should also be the case for lunch and breakfast.

3. Am I engaging in an event that is out of the ordinary?

Events by nature are for entertainment.

4. Am I eating with people I do not interact with on a daily basis?

Sharing a meal with friends is definitely for entertainment. However, this is where you need to differentiate how frequently you eat with a particular group. For example, if you eat lunch with a group of friends every day, then those routine occasions should no longer be considered entertainment.

5. Am I being offered a food item as part of a celebration?

Often, we find ourselves tempted by foods that we do not plan into our day. For example, food is often passed around or shared at the office. Before eating unplanned food, ask yourself, "Is this food part of a celebration?" If it is to celebrate some event, enjoy a few bites. However, if it is not part of a celebration, ask yourself, "Will this food fuel my body?" If the answer is no, then you have the choice to pass on it.

6. Have I eaten for fuel all day, but feel like I could use a little spark to finish the day?

If you have eaten sensibly all day, then you have a little room for something out of the ordinary. This is your opportunity for a planned indulgence; like a square of dark chocolate or a few planned bites of dessert.

This new way of looking at food helped me to put food into proper perspective. Asking yourself these few questions allows you to adjust your expectations to suit the situation. Moreover, you have more leeway in your weekly intake to occasionally eat richer foods as long as you have eaten sensibly the majority of the time.

Stop and Think: Recognize and Acknowledge Your Mental Blocks

By this point you should already be well into your journaling. As you read through the three mental blocks you likely identified with one or all of them. The following worksheet will help you to pinpoint specific ways your mental blocks about food have caused you to act in the past.

Take a moment to stop and consider how these mental blocks may be hindering you from developing healthy weight thinking. You will want to revisit this section again as you progress with your journal.

1. We have looked at three common mental blocks to success with weight. Write down some specific examples (as you notice them in your journaling) of how these mental blocks affect or have affected your food choices.

    a.   Learned Helplessness

_____

_____

_____

    b.   Short-Term Mentality

_____

_____

_____

    c.   Entertainment vs Fuel Dilemma

_____

_____

_____

2.   Have you uncovered a mental block other than the three mentioned? If so, what have you discovered? (Other possible mental blocks: starving children / clean your plate mentality or the idea that food is love)

_____

_____

_____

3.   Come up with a personal phrase you will say to yourself when you come up against a mental block.

_____

_____

_____

4. What are some specific actions you can take to counter
   your mental block (these can be ones I've suggested in
   this book or another that's better suited to you)?

   _____

   _____

   _____

Action Steps to Conquer My Mental Block

What Is Your Mental Block?

Action Steps

1. _____

2. _____

3. _____

4. _____

5. _____

Some Practical Ways To Battle Your Mental Blocks

When it comes to food, there's a lot to be said for the phrase,
"it's all in your head," because our satisfaction with food is largely
based on what we think and perceive. We have to convince
ourselves that we can be satisfied with less than our stomachs are
trained to expect.

Abandon the Idea of Fullness as a Gauge

People often eat until they feel full, but this may not be the best indicator when you are first trying to alter your eating habits toward losing weight. If you are relying on fullness as a signal to stop eating, then you are likely overeating at this beginning stage of your journey.

Usually, the stomach stretches as it is filled with food. It then sends signals to the brain to tell you it's full. However, when you are first trying to lose weight, your stomach will be accustomed to larger amounts of food.

Consequently, you need to develop new expectations for your eating. Fullness is often accompanied by feelings of lethargy and an inability to move freely. That's why some people find it necessary to unbutton the top button of their pants after a meal.

It's possible to overeat for so long that these feelings are expected as normal outcomes of a satisfying meal. In essence, we train ourselves to expect this overfull feeling every time we eat.

Of course, you expect to eat less when you are trying to lose weight; however, smaller food portions are unlikely to cause that full feeling you are accustomed to.

Practical Step
Add More Free Foods To Trigger Fullness

A good way to remedy the "empty tummy" feeling is to add a sizable portion of free foods to each meal. Free foods are high-fiber, low-calorie foods. For example, add extra veggies to your meal.

Vegetables will not only help stretch your stomach to trigger the full feeling; they also add extra fiber to your meal that will cause you to feel satisfied longer. Another problem with relying on the physical signal of fullness to stop eating is that the food may not actually reach your stomach to give you the sensation of fullness until after you have finished eating. This is because the food has to make its way down the digestive track. It usually takes 20 minutes for the brain to register fullness after you eat.

Practical Step
Eat Slower

One way to make the meal last longer is to divide it into courses. Instead of eating everything on one plate, consider eating a soup or salad before you eat your main meal. This is an especially helpful strategy when dining out at a buffet-style restaurant.

Instead of a visual signal, try developing a mental picture of what a correct portion size should look like and then stop eating after you have consumed it. We often underestimate the serving sizes of the foods we eat.

Practical Step
Know Correct Visual Comparisons

Refer to the visual comparison table in chapter six. Print this chart and refer to it regularly during the first several weeks of habit formation. Eventually you will reframe your thinking to accept the new portion sizes as normal.

Keep in mind that restaurant portions are often huge! We want to feel like we get value for our money, so restaurants charge a lot and give a lot in exchange.

Practical Step
Expect Restaurant Portions To Be Too Large

Plan to share a restaurant meal or box up half at the beginning of the meal to remove the temptation.

Mind Hacks

What if I told you that you could benefit from a little slight of hand or should I say slight of mind?

The battle of weight is won in the mind. When in the midst of cutting back on your food intake, you are fighting to break long-held ideas of how much food it takes for you to feel satisfied. Often, you will find that the amount of food your body actually needs to function properly is considerably less than the amounts you are used to eating.

I've learned that it's not so much the food, but what I think about the food that really matters. For this reason, I've developed a number of mind hacks that work for weight loss. These can help you navigate the path of eating with awareness. They really help me "be" satisfied with lesser amounts of food. So yes, I have tricked myself into satisfaction and it has worked like a dream.

Bite Trading

This trick works well when you are dining out with someone else who is not watching every bite; like your kids, husband or boyfriend. Order the more sensible option and then trade them for a few bites of their richer entree.

It is amazing how satisfied you feel when you know that you can still have a few bites of your favorite foods. The key here is to eat only a few bites, not half, of the richer entree.

Sizing Up

This hack works well with food that comes in pieces, like pizza or nuggets of chicken. Here, you purposely size up the food and choose to eat the smaller pieces.

I employ this hack when eating pizza. It is one of the foods that I find hardest to resist. My mind just doesn't seem satisfied with less than three pieces, so I intentionally chose the three smallest pieces. When all is said and done, my mind is satisfied that I had three pieces even when the actual combined amount is closer to two.

1/2s to 1/4s

We know that reducing portion size is essential for weight loss, but it feels so deflating to look down at a plate with significantly less food than you are used to eating; especially when you know you don't get to eat any more. This is where the 1/2's to 1/4's mind hack comes in handy.

Instead of serving yourself the entire reduced portion all at once, determine how much you are going to eat and then, serve yourself half of that. Yes, you will end up with a tiny amount on your plate, BUT you are setting up a scenario where you get to go back for seconds.

The idea of seconds lessens the feeling of deprivation, because you allowed yourself the controlled indulgence of extra food.

Downsizing

There is a commonly known psychological effect called the Delboeuf Illusion in which people are likely to misjudge the size of identical circles when one circle is surrounded by a larger circle.

Blank space plays tricks on our minds and causes us to perceive an item as smaller when it's surrounded by empty space.

> ...in a study conducted at a health and fitness camp, campers who were given larger bowls served and consumed 16% more cereal than those given smaller bowls. Despite the fact that those campers were eating more, their estimates of their cereal consumption were 7% lower than the estimates of the group eating from the smaller bowls. This suggests that not only could large dinnerware cause us to serve and eat more; it can do so without us noticing and trick us into believing we have eaten less.[16]

The size of the plate or bowl makes a huge difference in our perception of portion sizes. Try downsizing your plate size to bring your portions into perspective.

Select and Savor

Are you guilty of eating too quickly? Fast eating causes you to polish off a meal before your mind has even had time to register the experience or the calorie consumption. Instead, try to select and savor each bite of a meal or snack.

Eat one piece at a time; taking special care to fully chew and appreciate the flavor of the food. If you are eating with a fork, make sure to put the fork down between each bite. This hack helps to curb the need for speed and increases the enjoyment level of each bite.

Chapter 6

Overcoming Our Food Excuses

IN THE LAST CHAPTER, WE looked at the mental blocks that hinder our relationship with food. These mental blocks prevent us from taking a leading role in our own food choices. Our mental blocks typically cause us to approach food with a certain set of expectations and assumptions.

For example, learned helplessness convinces you that certain situations are irresistible. Consequently you behave in a way that suggests you have no control over your actions. Or, you assume that your food should always entertain you, which causes you to eat more than you should or seek out unhealthy food choices that better stimulate the pleasure centers in your brain.

In this chapter, we want to break down our food behavior one more step by exploring the excuses we use to validate our actions with food. We have to acknowledge and address our excuses before we can overcome them.

I have heard it and I have said it many times, "I've got to go on a diet to get this weight off!" If I can just find that right diet, that right food combination, then I can finally rid myself of the weight. I think what I was, and so many of us are still missing is the fact that the weight and overeating are really only symptoms of something else.

What happens when we focus only on the symptom of weight?

Let me share an example from my past to help bring this idea of addressing the symptom rather than the cause into sharper focus. About ten years ago, I went through quite an ordeal before finally being diagnosed with iron deficiency anemia. Prior to my diagnosis, I incrementally lost my desire and motivation to do activities I typically enjoyed. Yet, nothing in me signaled that something was amiss. I just settled in and accepted my new routine.

> We have to acknowledge and address our excuses before we can overcome them.

The turning point came when I began to lose my hair. Of course we all experience hair fall on a daily basis, but I was soon noticing the sink fill every time I fixed my hair, not to mention the hair I was cleaning out of the tub drain. Now, THIS new scenario got my full attention! I guess I can give a shout-out to vanity at this point. I was losing my hair and a lot of it and that was not ok. Of course, I did what we all do in cases like this; I went straight to my computer and typed in hair loss.

I should mention something very important at this stage. One might think that I coupled the terms fatigue and hair loss in my search; however, at the time I did not even remotely associate the two symptoms. After a thorough search I settled on a dermatologist as my first line of attack to deal with my hair loss. This misstep would result in 6 more months of hair loss and worsening fatigue because the dermatologists had no idea what was wrong with me.

By this point I had lost about forty percent of my hair and I was becoming increasingly worried and discouraged. Then, I made the pivotal decision to give a general practitioner a try, which proved to be the right one.

Unlike the dermatologists who focused immediately on the symptom of hair loss, the general practitioner sat me down and asked a series of probing questions about all facets of my life. Only then did it come out that I was experiencing hair loss and extreme fatigue. He then zeroed in on iron deficiency as a possible cause for these symptoms and I eventually came back from virtually zero iron storage.

I was so concerned with the hair loss that I put all of my energy into finding a cure for it. But all those hair loss creams and pills did absolutely nothing to stop my hair from falling out. Why? Because my hair loss was only a symptom of a bigger problem!

We hate to think that our problem is about more than food. I know, I know we don't want to think that it goes deeper and a lot of us really don't connect with things that we perceive as too touchy-feely. But, unfortunately it's time for some tough love: if you can't control the food that you place in your mouth, for whatever reason, then you have a problem that goes deeper than the food itself.

Ouch!! I know that hurts. We want to believe it's anything but us. Maybe I have a slow metabolism, poor genes, or a medical condition; anything but the fact that, just maybe, I have something going on in my head that goes beyond the food itself. Are there people who have medical conditions that make it difficult to control their weight? Yes, there are some. Do some people have a genetic predisposition to carry more weight or a slower metabolism that has existed since early childhood? Yes, undoubtedly this is the case for a small percentage of people.

We hate to think that our problem is about more than food.

That leaves the rest of us armed with our excuses. I was the same way, so I know exactly what you're thinking. On 10 separate occasions in my past I dieted and lost at least 25 pounds up to 40 pounds on a diet. Each and every time I told myself that would be the last time, and each time, I reverted back to the same old excuses and habits.

Each time I set out, armed with nutritional knowledge and my good intentions. I employed the traditional take on weight, which relied heavily on rules and lists of foods to stay away from at all costs.

While these rules kept me on the straight and narrow just long enough to lose some weight, they lacked staying power because I never addressed why I eat.

The teachings of the New Testament consistently call us to evaluate our hearts and our motives. Let's look at Colossians 2: 20 – 23,

> [20]Since you died with Christ to the basic principles of this world, why, as though you still belonged to it, do you submit to its rules: [21]"Do not handle! Do not taste! Do not touch!"? [22]These are all destined to perish with use, because they are based on human commands and teachings. [23]Such regulations indeed have an appearance of wisdom, with their self-imposed worship, their false humility and their harsh treatment of the body, but they lack any value in restraining sensual indulgence.

While we can follow a list of rules for the short-term goal of losing weight, those rules will never sufficiently transform our behavior because they "lack any value in restraining sensual indulgence." Eventually, we just revert back to our same excuses for allowing food to dictate our actions.

It's time to tackle the top four excuses for being overweight and how to move on with action steps specifically targeted for each of these excuses. These steps will focus on eating with awareness and will help you develop a new outlook on your food choices.

God can give you a new perspective on food. Rather than relegating your food choices to a list of rules, shoulds and should-nots, you can choose to exercise your freedom in Christ. "It is for freedom that Christ has set us free. Stand firm, then, and do not let yourselves be burdened by a yoke of slavery." (Galatians 5:1, NIV)

Christ's finished work on the cross secured your freedom as an heir to God's kingdom and a beneficiary of His many promises. Still, you have to make the conscious decision to view your food choices as opportunities to exercise your God-given freedom, rather than as a burden you must bear. Otherwise, you will fall right back to hiding behind your excuses.

Top 4 Excuses for Being Overweight

1. I Eat Because I Am Bored.

2. I Eat Because I Like the Taste of Food.

3. I Eat When I Am Stressed.

4. I Eat Because the Food Is There.

Excuse: I Eat Because I am Bored.

We all know the drill. You're sitting down in the living room watching a television program or surfing the web when your mind suddenly drifts to food. So, you get up from your chair and head off in the direction of the kitchen to meet the immediate need.

This is a very typical pattern for a lot of us. One of the most common excuses for being overweight is – I Eat Because I Am Bored. Initially, this excuse sounds plausible until you consider the myriad of activities you could engage in when bored.

- Go for a walk.

- Call, text, or tweet a friend.

- Read a book.

- Clean something.

- Organize something.

- Research an upcoming vacation.

- Paint your nails.

- Wash the car.

- Paint or draw a picture.

- Give yourself a facial.

- Brush your teeth.

- Look through your closet for new wardrobe combinations.

You get the point. I just listed 12 activities that do not involve food in any way. The reason why people who have weight problems gravitate immediately to thoughts of food when they are bored is because they have trained themselves to look to food as the answer to their every whim.

This goes back to the entertainment vs. fuel dilemma. Basically, bored eaters look to food as their primary source of entertainment. Consequently, when they feel even the slightest twinge of dissatisfaction with an activity or when they allow their mind to wander, it immediately goes to food. Why?...because food is seen only in terms of its entertainment value, rather than a necessary source of fuel for the body.

Solutions to Break the Bored-Eating Cycle and Move On and Lose Weight for Good

Short-Circuit the "Immediate Eat" Response

Most overeating is mindless eating with no awareness. You have conditioned yourself to turn to food any time your mind or attention is not focused on something else. A weight loss mentality is established through a pattern of eating with awareness.

Most overeating is mindless eating with no awareness.

Practical Step

First, institute a pause and question time between the thought and the response. When the thought of food comes to mind, ask yourself a series of questions.

Am I really hungry or just bored?
When was the last time I ate?
Am I experiencing any physical sensations of hunger (growling stomach, headache?)

If your first answer is boredom, you need to predetermine some activities to engage in when you feel the temptation to eat, particularly activities that keep you away from the kitchen.

It is also important to consider when you ate last. It is reasonable to feel some hunger if you have not eaten for 3 or more hours, especially when you are first weaning yourself from the bored-eat response. If it has been several hours, then you can allow yourself to have a nutritious, measured snack. Remember, experiencing intense physical sensations of hunger is counterproductive for establishing new positive thinking and healthy patterns with food.

Stop Looking to Food as a Source of Entertainment

Yes, there are times when food is and should be a wonderful source of entertainment and community, but it should not be every time you put something in your mouth. When we eat out of boredom, we often gravitate to junk foods or sweets because they appeal to the pleasure centers in the brain. In other words, you are looking for something to stimulate you.

Practical Step
Find Another Go-To-Activity

Here is where it is extremely helpful to find some activity that distracts you and captivates your attention away from thoughts of food. Can you think of an activity that interests you? It takes a while to wean yourself from the emotional hunger response and it helps immensely to have something else to devote your energy to besides food.

If you devote yourself to this activity for a prolonged period of several weeks, every time you feel the boredom coming on, you will notice that the emotional hunger response will become less and less intense as you slowly train your body.

Let's consider some of the activities listed earlier in this section.

1. Go for a walk.

Remove yourself from temptation and flee from the fridge. It's time to get the blood pumping a little bit. Walking helps to clear your head and it stimulates your other senses as well. Plus, walking actually provides a fitness benefit, so you are essentially killing two birds with one stone.

2. Call, text, or tweet a friend.

Your mind drifts to food because you want stimulation, so you need to search elsewhere than the kitchen. Use your food cravings as a reminder to reach out to others. A good conversation can do wonders for redirecting your attention.

3. Clean something.

It's funny how quickly our mind turns to food and how slowly it considers cleaning the kitchen floor!

4. Organize something.

Consider that stack of old pictures, the pile of shoes in

your closet or that jumble of plastic containers in your kitchen cabinets. Taking the time to organize something brings order into your life in some small way.

Actually, an increased sense of order can also spill over into your thinking. Some people turn to food because they can't take the messiness or chaos of things around them. By taking control of some aspect of your life, even if it is only matching the proper lid to its corresponding container, you gain a sense of accomplishment that eating a bag of chips can't supply.

An increased sense of order can also spill over into your own thinking.

5. Research an upcoming vacation.

Find something else to get excited about that doesn't involve food. Start researching for an upcoming vacation. Look for hotel deals, attraction discounts, and tourist reviews.

6. Paint your nails.

Painting your own nails takes time and concentration. Not only that, but you can save a good bit of money by doing them yourself. You can use the money you save to go on that vacation you're planning!

7. Give yourself a facial.

The internet is full of natural concoctions for various facial scrubs, moisturizers, and masks. Instead of going to the kitchen for a snack, round up some food ingredients and do a DIY facial.

8. Brush your teeth.

Brushing your teeth actually works on several levels. The taste and smell of peppermint are known to boost mood. But even better, a lot of foods just don't taste that great on top of minty-fresh breath.

9. Look through your closet for new wardrobe combinations.

For women, clothes are one of the few things that can run a close second to food and may even inch it out from time to time. Look through your closet for new wardrobe combinations. Mix and match different separates that you have never tried before. You can also look at your favorite blogs or the internet for inspiration. Find inspiration outfits and then try to copy them with items you already own.

All of these are great ways to get your mind off food, but first you have to short circuit the immediate eat response. The time to come up with alternative activities to eating is BEFORE you put any food in your mouth. Snacking is often an unconscious activity. You grab a bag of chips and before you know it, half the bag is gone and you can hardly remember it going in.

The good news is this—once you have trained yourself to recognize your tendency to eat when you're bored, you can actually develop a habit of listening to your stomach for cues of when to eat.

Practical Step
Drink a Full Glass of Water

Finally, keep a large glass on your kitchen counter. Anytime you feel bored, go into the kitchen, fill the glass with water and drink it all. Sometimes, you are experiencing a physiological need, but it is often thirst, rather than actual hunger.

Remember when you were little and you would look up at your mom and say, "I'm bored." What would she say in response? My mother would always say, "You better go find something to do or I'll give you something to keep you busy."

So, now we're all adults, but it doesn't mean we have learned that lesson. Even if you go into the kitchen to eat an entire bag of chips, if you were really bored before, you'll be just as bored when you return to your previous activity.

Excuse: I Eat Because I Like the Taste of Food.

For some of us, there really isn't a deep, emotional issue that we can pin our eating on. We could sit in front of a counselor and pour out our hearts, but in the end we would find out that we eat because we are motivated by food's sheer yumminess.

So, what in the world do you do with this?

First of all, people who can't seem to resist the intoxicating draw of food need to look at food as their drug of choice. Just as the alcoholic craves his liquor and the drug addict craves her fix, so the food addict craves food.

Experiments with animals and humans show that, for some people, the same reward and pleasure centers of the brain that are triggered by addictive drugs, like cocaine and heroin, are also activated by food, especially highly palatable foods. Highly palatable foods are foods rich in sugar, fat, and salt.

Is the intoxicating draw of food like a drug for you?

Like addictive drugs, highly palatable foods trigger feel-good brain chemicals such as dopamine. Once people experience the pleasure associated with increased dopamine transmission in the brain's reward pathway from eating certain foods, they quickly feel the need to eat again.

The reward signals from highly palatable foods may override other signals of fullness and satisfaction. As a result, people keep eating, even when they're not hungry. People who show signs of food addiction may also develop a tolerance to food. They eat more and more, only to find that food satisfies them less and less.[17]

The overeater who is totally motivated by taste likely has no off switch and seldom gets to the point of feeling full. However, unlike with alcohol and drugs that have the inherent power to derail a person's life or end it, the food addict is all-too-aware that an extra candy bar is unlikely to leave him passed out on the bathroom floor. Consequently, while food addiction operates on the same premise, it doesn't always yield the same life-shattering consequences. Of course, I am speaking in rather broad generalities. For the morbidly obese person, the threat to life comes much more into focus, but that is another subject entirely.

My own overeating tendencies definitely fall into the boredom/food-tastes-good category. This is good news for you because I have established workable, focused eating practices that address these two specific triggers for overeating.

Solutions to Break the Yummy Food Eating Cycle and Move On to Lose the Weight for Good

Acknowledge that You Have a Self-Control Problem

Why is it important to acknowledge that you have no self-control? Largely, it's because of our tendency to pass blame, rather than taking personal responsibility for our actions. Actually, when you say that a food was just too good to resist, you, in essence, shift the blame from yourself to the food. In so doing, you view your actions and food choices externally or separate from yourself: the food was so yummy, it made me eat it.

Your journaling is an effective tool for conquering your food issues and for establishing renewed weight loss thinking. By writing down your thoughts, expectations, and self-talk about food, you begin to see a truer picture of how your mind works and reacts to food.

Learn to Differentiate Those Times When Food is for Fuel and When it is for Entertainment

We've discussed how the Fuel vs. Entertainment Dilemma is a mental block that causes you to turn to food as a solution to boredom. Let's reiterate this point in response to the excuse that the food is just too tasty to resist.

Practical Step
Ask Yourself, "Why am I eating?"

Before a meal, ask yourself, "Is this for fuel or entertainment?" If the answer is fuel, then stick to the basics by making food choices that will satisfy your hunger without adding a lot of excess fat or calories. However, if you are out with family or friends and the answer is entertainment, then allow yourself extended grace to eat richer options (still keeping portion size in mind) and enjoy the event.

This weight loss mindset does not shut the door on all yummy food. Instead, it allows for opportunities to enjoy food for it's yumminess value on certain occasions. Establishing an everyday habit of eating for fuel allows you to bank a calorie deficit to make up for entertainment eating.

Now, before you do the happy dance and take this as an all-express pass to eat yourself crazy when it's for entertainment, remember eating with awareness has to become a lifestyle regardless of the type of food you are eating.

Establish the Habit of Portioning Out Your Food Before You Eat It

We have already established that the overeater who is inspired by the taste of food typically runs low on self-control. As such, ridding one's kitchen of every tidbit of delicious food is likely to backfire in the long-run. Why? Because you are motivated and inspired by the taste of food! It is more realistic to develop the focused eating habit of pre-portioning your food before ever taking a bite.

For example, you are dying for a candy bar. Yes, the healthiest option would be to say no to candy bars forever, from this point on. However, a more realistic approach would be to half the candy bar, put the rest away and sit down to enjoy the chocolate with focused awareness.

Practical Step
Pre-Portioning

- Never eat directly from the bag.
- Never expect to eat a whole entree at a typical dining establishment.

- Count out a specific number of snack items (I count out almonds and potato chips!).

- Know the visual equivalents for commonly eaten foods (Ex. 1/2 cup of rice is comparable to a rounded handful).

- Remove your plate from the table once your portion is consumed.

Excuse: I Overeat When I am Stressed

It's not surprising that people feel stressed out and overwhelmed in our modern-day society. Life rushes by at a constant clip and we are expected to move right along with it. Although technology makes many life tasks easier, it also makes us feel like we have to be plugged in all the time!

So, how does all this stress affect our weight? One common defense mechanism is the fight or flight mode. This is the tendency to either stand up to your problems and responsibilities or run from them. All of us cope with stress differently. Some of us stand up to the problem, look it squarely in the eye and deal with it without another thought. Others of us find it difficult to process stressful events, so we're tempted to bolt whenever we feel overwhelmed.

And where does the stress eater run? Yep, straight to food. Food provides immediate satisfaction and, most importantly, it doesn't talk back. But, while it may not talk out loud, it can wreck serious havoc on your metabolism. How does stress affect our metabolism?

Studies have shown that hormones play a role in elevating the desire to eat foods containing carbohydrates during prolonged periods of stress. When our brains receive stimuli that indicate a period of stress on the body, they respond by releasing cortisol, a hormone whose primary function is to raise blood sugar and promote the metabolism of carbohydrates, protein and fat. In response to higher blood sugar levels, the pancreas releases extra insulin, which has the effect of lowering blood sugar rather quickly. This, in turn, causes a craving for foods rich in carbohydrates–e.g., comfort foods.[18]

Food provides immediate satisfaction because it stimulates the pleasure sensors in our brains and, most importantly, it doesn't talk back.

Not only does stress eating affect our metabolism, but it short-circuits our pathway to God. He is ready to be our ultimate stress-reliever, but we seldom make it to Him with our problems. Instead, we look to food to sooth us or divert our attention from stressful situations.

Too often, we forget that Jesus lived and walked on this earth just like we do. He really can identify with our struggles and our emotions.

"We do not have a high priest who is unable to empathize with our weaknesses, but we have one who has been tempted in every way, just as we are—yet he did not sin." (Hebrews 4:15, NIV) But, He can't help us work through our problems if we keep running to food for an emotional fix.

Solutions to Break the Stressed Eating Cycle and Move On to Lose the Weight for Good

Do Not Allow Yourself to Become Hungry.

Hunger itself produces stress. Hunger is your body's way of signaling that your fuel tank is empty and needs refilling. Actually, the physiological feelings of hunger can closely resemble our physiological response to stress: irritability, inability to think clearly, and light-headedness. Now, pair the natural feelings of hunger with a stressful situation and you have the perfect breeding ground for poor food choices.

Practical Step

It helps to take hunger out of the picture. Make sure you plan healthy, satisfying snacks to be eaten throughout the day at 2-to-3-hour intervals. Make sure that these snacks are rich in fiber and protein and low in sugar.

I highly recommend nuts (a measured amount) as a go-to snack because they satisfy hunger and consist of healthy fats. If your body is well-satisfied, you will have more energy and attention to focus on the element of stress.

Recognize Your Physiological Triggers to Stress

All of us react differently to stress. For some, stress can interfere with their concentration (reading over the same page multiple times), others may notice a slight tremor in their hands, and still others react by becoming increasingly agitated or easily provoked.

Practical Step
Identify Your Stress Response

If you are a stress eater, it is helpful to pinpoint your stress response. Think about times when you feel extremely stressed. How do you typically react? Does stress often affect you in a particular way physically? Identifying your physical response to stress will better equip you to deal with the stress in positive ways that do not involve food.

Predetermine an Activity to Perform When You Notice Your Stress Response

You have figured out your stress response, now what? You need to predetermine a calming action. It can seem counterproductive to take a time-out when you are stressed with too much to do.

However, performing a calming action gives you the focused opportunity to acknowledge your stress and deal with it proactively.

Practical Step

Calming Action

Here are some possible calming activities (several of these can also be performed simultaneously):

- PRAY

- Remove yourself from your location. Walk around the block or the office. (Physical exercise releases feel-good endorphins)

- Take some deep breaths.

- Recite a favorite poem or Bible verse.

- Listen to a song or sing a chorus.

- Flip through a slideshow of your favorite pictures.

- Chew a piece of peppermint/spearmint gum.

- Journal your immediate thoughts or frustrations.

- Repeat a memorized passage of Scripture.

- Call and vent to your spouse or friend. (Preferably someone who is not involved with the situation. They can provide perspective. Note: Do not go to the same friend repeatedly as this can wear them out.)

- Table the stressful activity, if possible, to allow yourself time to reflect and brainstorm an effective resolution.

Practical Step

Now, in terms of overeating, here is the key. You must vow to yourself that you will not resort to food before you have performed a calming activity. Wait to eat until you are no longer experiencing the physiological response.

This will help to reinforce the habit of eating with awareness. Reducing stress will not only help you bring your weight in check; it will also enhance your outlook and relationships.

Excuse: I Eat Because the Food is There.

Did you grow up hearing your mom say, "Eat all of the food on your plate"? The compulsion to eat food just because it's there often comes from a good place. We know that there are people in the world who never know where their next meal is coming from. Consequently, the thought of wasting or passing on food can become a moral conflict.

It's amazing how much emotion is wrapped up in our food choices. Too often we serve up our food based on long-held assumptions of what our body needs to be satisfied. The truth is that our body often needs far less than we think it does. Actually, portion sizes have steadily increased over the last twenty years. What we now perceive as a normal portion is considerably more than we should be eating. In other words, the amount your mom may have encouraged you to eat has morphed into considerably more food at each sitting.

Average portion sizes have grown so much over the past 20 years that sometimes the plate arrives and there's enough food for two or even three people on it. Growing restaurant portion sizes have affected what Americans think of as a "normal" portion at home. We call it portion distortion.[19]

Eating with awareness is essential for fighting the compulsion to eat the food just because it's there. You need to know how much you are going to eat before you take the first bite. This will keep you from putting more on your plate than you should eat in one sitting.

	20 Years Ago		*Today*	
	Portion	*Calories*	*Portion*	*Calories*
Bagel	3" diameter	140	6" diameter	350
Cheese-burger	1	333	1	590
Spaghetti with meatballs	1 cup sauce 3 small meatballs	500	2 cups sauce 3 large meatballs	1,020
Soda	6.5 ounces	82	20 ounces	250
Blueberry muffin	1.5 ounces	210	5 ounces	500

Solutions for Eating Just Because the Food is There

Practical Step
Learn What Appropriate Serving Sizes Actually Look Like.

The serving size graphic on the next page provides some very helpful visual comparisons. Refer to it regularly until you have memorized the appropriate serving sizes.

You have grown accustomed to seeing a certain amount of food on your plate. Also, your stomach is accustomed to larger amounts of food, which means you may have conditioned yourself to stop only when you feel full and slightly uncomfortable. Recognize how eating less makes you feel and what smaller portions look like on a plate.

1. *Learn to read food labels.*
   Snack foods are often packaged in bags with multiple servings.
2. *Avoid anything that is labeled supersized.*
3. *Eat from a smaller sized plate.*

Realize that the amount you eat or don't eat will not provide any additional food for the children in Africa or those starving in many of our urban centers. If it is really a conscience issue for you, then consider doing something proactively to feed the poor. Donate your time and/or money to charitable pursuits.

VISUAL COMPARISON

A guide (based on standards that most nutritionists follow) of what a typical serving should look like.[20]

steak = small iPhone	cheese = matchbox
pancake = DVD	pasta = ice cream scoop
potato = mouse	fish = checkbook
butter = postage stamp	salad dressing = 1-oz shot glass
rice = baseball	peanut butter = golf ball
beans = lightbulb	dark chocolate = dental floss

Skip a few tempting restaurant meals, especially when you are first trying to develop a weight loss mindset, and give that money to feed those who don't have food.

Which excuse or excuses do you relate to the most?

Can you think of specific examples from your journaling where you have made one of these excuses?

Make a conscious effort in the next 3 days to look for evidence of your excuse or excuses in your behavior with food. Write down the thoughts that come into your head when you are tempted to give in to the draw of food. Commit to take your excuses to God. Ask Him to open your eyes to those times when you look to food, rather than drawing closer to Him.

Chapter 7

Overcoming Hurdles To Fitness Motivation

DEALING WITH EXERCISE AND OTHER ELEMENTS associated with general fitness can be even harder than wrapping our heads around food because some of us never really "feel" like exercising. Or, we tell ourselves we just don't have the energy or the time. Food is not the only area where our behavior follows our thinking.

Still, we are reminded that, "in him we live and move and have our being." (Acts 17:28, NIV) We literally would not have breath in our lungs if God did not provide it. Nor could we do any other of the myriad of daily activities that we convince ourselves are essential to our life and existence. It just makes sense to care for our bodies if we want to live the full life God desires to give us.

God's word says that we are fearfully and wonderfully made. As such, our bodies are created to work as a coordinated whole. While nutrition is a vital ingredient for a healthy lifestyle, it would be a mistake to assume that food alone determines how well our bodies function.

Motivation Sappers for Overall Fitness

When you feel you are lacking the energy or motivation to carry through with your fitness goals, ask yourself these questions:

- Have I struggled with similar motivation issues in the last 7 days?

- Have I been getting enough sleep?

- Have I been remembering to drink water?

- Have I picked the wrong time of day to exercise?

Motivation Sapper: General Lack of Motivation

If you regularly suffer from the same lack of motivation, then this is likely a "pick yourself up by your bootstraps" kind of moment. You need more gym time instead of less. For some of us, exercise falls more into the category of necessary tasks, like brushing your teeth and going to the bathroom. You may not have the time or inclination, but your body will suffer if you neglect it.

In Him we live and move and have our being.
ACTS 17:28

Practical Step

Join A Group Exercise Activity To Increase Motivation

I find that I am much more motivated in a group, so I do most of my exercise in a group setting.

A group setting increases motivation for several reasons:

- You generally have to pay something for group classes or organized sports. If you don't attend, then you are wasting your money.

- This setting feeds the competitive element. While you may not be competing one-on-one, group classes motivate you to at least keep up with your peers for face saving.

- On the same line, you will often push yourself more if you have a teacher and a specified class time.

- If you have joined an organized sport, then you let your teammates down when you don't attend.

- Group classes add a social element that you do not get when exercising alone.

- Even adding one additional person (for walking or biking) makes the time pass faster.

Motivation Sapper: Not Getting Enough Sleep

Some of us have a difficult time summoning motivation to exercise on the best of days, but add on a few too many sleepless nights and we are looking for any excuse to skip the gym. Lack of sleep can derail our exercise goals.

We all know sleep is important. The typical adult needs between 7 to 9 hours of sleep a night, but this stretch of time can often seem elusive. In fact, a lot of us are running at a sleep deficit. According to the Center For Disease Control, thirty percent of Americans reported receiving less than six hours per night in response to a National Health Interview Survey.[21]

So, how are those lost hours of sleep affecting our bodies?

The Effects of Lack of Sleep

1. Decreased Energy and Motivation

Lack of sleep makes you feel fuzzy. It impairs your ability to concentrate and think clearly. This can significantly affect your ability to prioritize your time and envision your fitness goals. Again, this is where focused awareness comes into play. If you are not well rested, it will be harder to think through the ramifications of a missed workout, or two, or three...

2. Slower Metabolism

Lack of sleep disrupts the chemical processes in our system.

The two hormones that are key in this process are ghrelin and leptin. "Ghrelin is the 'go' hormone that tells you when to eat, and when you are sleep-deprived, you have more ghrelin," Breus says. "Leptin is the hormone that tells you to stop eating, and when you are sleep deprived, you have less leptin."

More ghrelin plus less leptin equals weight gain.

"You are eating more, plus your metabolism is slower when you are sleep-deprived," Breus says.[22]

In essence, this chemical disruption actually sets your body up to crave more food, which is the exact opposite of what you want to achieve. That means you could end up having to work out twice as hard to achieve the same results you would have if you were better rested.

3. Less Time for Your Body to Repair Itself

Your body uses your nightly sleep time to repair itself. This is the time your body secretes growth hormones to repair muscles and bones that were taxed during your previous exercise sessions.

Remember, muscle growth is actually a controlled injury. Each time you exercise a particular muscle group, small tears are formed in the muscle fiber. After exercise, the body repairs itself by creating new, stronger fibers to support the torn area.

Without proper sleep, your muscles do not have enough time to strengthen and repair as they should.

Consequently, you may feel weaker when you attempt to use those muscles again because they did not have adequate time to heal.

How to Get More Sleep

The bottom line is this—you have to prioritize your fitness goals and then develop action steps to meet those goals. If fitness is a priority for you, you will have to adjust your activities and your sleep schedule to meet that goal.

Practical Step
Predetermine a Bedtime

Determine when you need to go to bed to achieve the optimal amount of sleep. Keep in mind that every person has different sleep requirements. Then, make a conscious decision to stop all work, computer, or television viewing thirty minutes before that time. This helps to prepare your mind and body for rest—doing this will help set you on the right track.

Motivation Sapper: Not Drinking Enough Water

We all know that water is important for our bodies. It is a frequent message for any discussion on health and fitness. But, do we always listen? Personally, it's hard to get in the recommended amount of water every day, even though I know it's good for me. Often, my motivation for water consumption ebbs and flows.

Motivation also becomes a real consideration when it comes to exercise. In fact, dehydration can be a real motivation sapper for your fitness efforts. Lean muscle tissue is made up of 75% water, so your body needs fluid and lubrication for the muscles to respond properly.

Naturally, exercise causes your body to heat up. The body responds by creating perspiration to cool you down and maintain your body temperature. However, if you have not taken in enough water, dehydration can cause lowered energy, dizziness, and feelings of lethargy.

> Lean muscle tissue is made up of 75% water, so your body needs fluid and lubrication for the muscles to respond properly.

Feeling lightheaded during a workout is a sign of dehydration and a signal to tone it down a notch. Though willpower sometimes makes us want to push ourselves through a few more reps or another mile, feeling dizzy is an indicator that it's time to hydrate. "Due to the decreased plasma volume with dehydration during exercise," Casa says, "the heart must work harder to get blood to the working muscles." When there's not enough water in blood, both blood volume and blood pressure drop, resulting in dizziness.[23]

How Can You Make Sure You Are Getting Enough Water?

1. Make sure to check your urine.

Your urine should be a pale yellow color. If it has a concentrated color, this is a sign that you are not taking in enough water to flush out the impurities in your system.

2. Eat more fruits and vegetables if you are not a big water drinker.

Fruit and vegetables, depending on the variety, contain water and other electrolytes that your body needs. Some great water sources are lettuce, cucumbers, zucchini, radishes, celery, watermelon, strawberries, grapefruit, and tomatoes.

3. Supplement with other beverage alternatives.

There has always been quite a debate on whether or not caffeinated beverages actually help or hurt in terms of water intake. Caffeine does have diuretic properties, so will you just end up losing all the hydrating effect anyway? While water is still king for hydration, there is research to suggest that caffeinated beverages can provide hydrating benefits.

A review on the topic, which summarized numerous studies on the subject conducted over nearly 40 years, reported that taking in a large amount of caffeine at one time (around 300 mg, or what you'd get in 2-3 cups of strong coffee – and not an amount you'd drink all at once) can promote urination, but only in people who haven't had any caffeine for weeks. And those who are habitual caffeine consumers develop a tolerance to the diuretic effects – much like they develop a tolerance to the stimulating effects. The report also stated that "doses of caffeine equivalent to the amount normally found in standard servings of tea, coffee and carbonated soft drinks appear to have no diuretic action." So there you go; caffeinated beverages definitely "count" when it comes to meeting fluid needs.[24]

As a southern girl, I live and die by my iced tea! I have it for breakfast, lunch, and dinner. In fact, my friends expect iced tea when they come to my house. But, I have learned that the sweet iced tea of my youth is not the best alternative for drinking on a regular basis.

If you do choose tea or coffee as a supplemental water source, remember to curb the sugar. Drinking caffeinated drinks to increase your water intake is one thing, adding a considerable amount of sugar to these drinks is an entirely different ballgame. Remember, if

If you are going to consume sugar, a cupcake will be considerably more satisfying than wasting your empty sugar calories on your beverages.

you are going to consume sugar, a cupcake will be considerably more satisfying than wasting your empty sugar calories on your beverages.

4. Drink more water before, during, and after a workout.

Your body needs water to function properly. Drink an extra glass of water before you exercise. Take repeated sips of water at the slightest feeling of thirst. And then, drink a glass or two of water after a workout to replenish the liquid and electrolytes lost through perspiration.

At the gym I find it very easy to take in water because it is such a cool break from exercise. Seize on those opportunities when you feel a craving for water and take in as much as you can!

Motivation Sapper: Choosing the Wrong Time to Exercise

Everyone has their own opinions about the best time to exercise. The key is to find the best time that suits you and your schedule.

There really isn't any research to suggest that mornings or evenings are better suited for a workout. Generally, I like to exercise earlier in the day because I find that my motivation wanes as the day wears on.

2 Points to Consider When Choosing an Exercise Time

1. Body Rhythms

We all have our own body rhythms that determine our time for peak functioning and mental performance.

Circadian rhythm is governed by the 24-hour pattern of the earth's rotation. These rhythms influence body functions such as blood pressure, body temperature, hormone levels, and heart rate, all of which play a role in your body's readiness for exercise.

Using your body clock as a guide for when to go for a walk or hit the gym might seem like a good idea. But, of course, there are other important considerations, such as family and work schedules, or a friend's availability to walk with you.[25]

According to body rhythms, a morning person should exercise in the morning and a night owl should exercise at night. However, this does not always address other life realities.

2. Your Schedule

The best time to exercise is really the time you are most likely to do it. As I mentioned earlier, I prefer to exercise in the morning even though I am a night owl. Although I do find my mental energy and productivity to increase as the day progresses, I don't find this to be the case with my physical energy.

For one, I prefer to get my exercise done and behind me. Then, I can focus my attention on other things. Often, various unplanned chores and responsibilities crop up later in the day.

Since exercise is something you do largely for yourself, it can be tempting to place it on the back burner. However, without proper exercise, you may find that you have less stamina to process your other responsibilities effectively. Remember, getting the proper exercise really benefits everyone in your life because it helps your body and mind to run at peak efficiency.

For me, the evening is also the best time to prioritize time with my husband and family. So, I try to keep my evenings free. My one exception is an occasional evening walk with girlfriends. These walks are social/exercise activities that help me to connect with friends who help refuel me emotionally.

The key is finding a routine that you can stick to and incorporate into your life!

Remember Grace and Balance

Again, we should not deny the importance of grace and balance with our fitness, as well as, our food. So, what do you do when your week's routine derails your exercise routine?

1. Have a Back-up Plan

When I can't get to the gym, I rely on my Fitbit (pedometer) to log in steps for the day. On these movin' it days, it's not fancy, I just put on my tennis shoes and walk "laps" around my living room.

Maybe for you, movin' it might mean turning on some music and dancing a jig in the kitchen. While intensity is important for long-term fitness, your body still responds to physical movement regardless of what form it takes.

Utilizing data from the National Health and Nutrition Examination Survey, researchers measured the physical activity level of more than 10,500 Americans between 1999 and 2004...Among the 10,535 participants, there were a total of 665 deaths during the five-year study period. Not surprisingly, participants who met current exercise guidelines had the lowest risk of death compared to those who were less active. But getting some physical activity was better than none, according to findings. Participants meeting exercise guidelines had 36% lower risk of death and those who were active but didn't quite meet guidelines had 28% lower risk of death compared to subjects who got no exercise, whatsoever. And among adults who were active but didn't meet current guidelines, those who did muscle-strengthening activities like sit-ups had 44% lower risk of death than those who didn't.[26]

What is the take home message? When it comes to physical activity, we should get rid of the "all-or-nothing" mentality. Getting some physical activity is always better than none and according to this study, any amount of physical activity can help you live a longer life.

2.   Be Willing to Shake Things Up

You have to be willing to shake things up. For me, this means I have to pull my rear out of bed to attend a Saturday morning Zumba class when I've missed my normal weekly classes. Do I like to go to the gym on Saturday mornings? No…but I also accept that I am off my routine for the week and sometimes desperate times call for desperate measures.

3.   Accept That Life Happens

While it is important to set up an exercise routine, sometimes life happens and you can't make your exercise commitments regardless of your best intentions.

This is the time to extend a little grace. Don't allow yourself to become discouraged …attitude is half the battle of physical fitness. So, resist the temptation to hang it all up because you missed a few days. Take a cue from Scarlett O'Hara, "After all, tomorrow is another day."

Chapter 8

Habit Formation

IF ASKED, MOST OF US would agree that we want to develop better food habits. Stories of people who are healthy, fit, and strong inspire us. In fact, we are doubly impressed by those people who weren't healthy, fit, and strong, but then decided enough was enough and made the change.

So, what keeps us from getting out there and conquering the whole food thing once and for all? Of course, there isn't a one-size-fits-all answer to this question, but I think a lot of our success or subsequent failure at weight maintenance boils down to lack of habit formation. Once we determine to do something to change our fitness factor, do we actually do what it takes to develop sustainable habits?

Interestingly enough, many of us who struggle with weight also experience considerable success in other facets of our lives. In fact, weight woes seem to affect people of all stations, regardless of their considerable abilities or accomplishments in other areas.

Why is it that someone can experience such success in multiple areas of their life, but still struggle with keeping their weight in check?

Take a moment to think back to a major life accomplishment, possibly earning a degree or having your first child. Every notable life accomplishment shares some similar characteristics:

Weight woes seem to affect people of all stations. Regardless of their considerable abilities or accomplishments in other areas.

- **Start Date** – There was a distinctive moment when you decided, "I'm going to do this thing!"

- **Benchmarks** – There were steps that had to be overcome and built on from day-to-day and week-to-week. It didn't all come together at once.

- **Encouragement** – ...there was built-in encouragement. Sometimes it was external, like advice, grades, or compliments. Other times, you may have encouraged yourself for making it or rewarded yourself.

- **Learning Curve** – You understood that you didn't know everything there was to know when you got started. You realized that learning was part of the process and that you would make some mistakes along the way.

- **End Goal** – You started with a goal and were willing to put up with whatever it took to meet that goal.

When it comes to success, all of these factors help keep you on track from start to finish. What's more, they provide accountability to the task at hand. But, progress does not just happen…you have to establish a habitual routine to accomplish significant life goals.

Now, the majority of us would agree, albeit unwillingly, that weight is a major life consideration. However, unlike other significant milestones, we often don't regard our weight as a permanent state. For example, when we study to complete a degree, we don't intend to repeat the process again after an undetermined amount of time to relearn everything we learned the first time.

However, we often tend to place weight issues in a different category than many other significant life situations. In fact, we seem somewhat resolved to repeat the cycle over and over again. There is something about weight that many of us regard as temporary. Thus, when we lose the weight, in the back of our minds we just assume that it's just a matter of time before the weight comes back again.

Ephesians 4:22-24 prescribes two equal, but opposite actions required for effective habit formation, "You were taught, with regard to your former way of life, to put off your old self, which is being corrupted by its deceitful desires; to be made new in the attitude of your minds; and to put on the new self, created to be like God in true righteousness and holiness." In order to see lasting results, your new thinking about food and your behavior with it and around it must be translated into action and then, perpetually reinforced with new thoughtful habits.

Up to this point in your life, food has served a purpose. It has entertained you, soothed you, distracted you from other worries, comforted you and even given you something to exercise control over when you felt you had none. Food met various needs, albeit in an unhealthy, unproductive way. Still, you grew to trust it and rely on it.

So, don't think you can suddenly stop eating all the foods you love without consequences.

Instead, you must formulate new, sustainable habits or actions to address each of your old destructive habits. Essentially, the process looks like this:

1. You pinpoint a particular food behavior.

2. You explore the flawed or corrupted thinking that informed it.

3. You put off that behavior or habit; stop performing it.

4. You ask God to give you a new perspective or way of looking at the situation

5. You put on a new behavior/habit to replace the old, unhealthy behavior.

Developing a focused weight habit requires that you acknowledge that weight is indeed a significant factor worthy of dedicated time and consideration. Successful weight maintenance cannot be half-hearted, nor should it be viewed as a temporary fix; neither were any of your other notable life accomplishments.

Let's apply the common factors for notable life accomplishments to our weight.

Start Date

Significant change begins with focused attention and dedication. Establishing a successful weight journey cannot be just a side note to your life because then, it will never get your full attention or commitment.

Like other life accomplishments, such as the day you got married or had a child, there was no Plan B! Likewise, your weight loss efforts should be launched without a second option. If you want your weight loss to be forever, then it's time to start acting and thinking like it's forever.

Benchmarks

Fitness does not happen in a day. It involves a series of progressive steps. It's ok to be a beginner. Take on a learner mindset and expect to practice certain habits until you find what works for you. Also, set intermediate goals that build upon each other.

Successful weight maintenance cannot be half-hearted, nor should it be viewed as a temporary fix; neither were any of your other notable life accomplishments.

Encouragement

It helps to tell others about your new-found resolve. This builds in accountability. You need to find people who share your interests. If you plan to start off walking, then find a walking buddy who will commit to meet you several days a week.

You can also join an online fitness forum or purchase a Fitbit (pedometer). Some of you will find it extremely helpful to join a more organized weight loss program, like Weight Watchers, for the encouragement and accountability.

Learning Curve

Expect to have times when you feel like you don't know what you are doing, because sometimes you won't know what you're doing. If you were an expert in weight loss and management then you wouldn't need a lifestyle change. Instead, you are consciously trying to unlearn the bad habits that got you to this point and learn new ones to take their place.

For some of you, the concept of fitness will be a whole new ballgame. I have heard it said on multiple occasions, "I don't want to go to the gym because everyone is in better shape than me." First of all, everyone at the gym is somewhere on the same spectrum as you. What's more, the majority of people never step foot into a gym in the first place! You don't start out as an expert at anything and fitness is no exception. Allow yourself to learn, grow, and even fail a time or two.

End Goal

You need to know what you are doing it all for. Weight loss is a fine benchmark for fitness, but it should not be the end goal. Fitness is more about your mindset and overall health. Jesus warned His disciples, "…do not worry about your life, what you will eat; or about your body, what you will wear. Life is more than food, and the body more than clothes." (Luke 12:22-24, NIV) You want to invest yourself in something that will add value, not only to your life, but to the lives of those you love. As a child of Christ, your ultimate purpose is to live in relationship with Him; to hear His voice and to follow His will. This whole habit formation process will help navigate an obstacle that has consistently interfered with this relationship.

Seek Health, Not a Clothing Size

The idea of establishing an end goal brings up an important point for consideration. It can be very tempting to chase a particular clothing size when you are in the process of losing weight. However, clothing size does not necessarily represent health or fitness.

Part of establishing renewed weight loss thinking is establishing new focused eating habits and then allowing your body to adjust and change in response to those modifications to your diet.

The problem with chasing a size is that many people set up size expectations that can only be achieved by strict deprivation dieting. Reaching a particular size may bring a sense of accomplishment in the short run, but these feelings will be short-lived if you can't maintain your new weight for the long haul. What's more, our body changes at different stages of our lives, which may necessitate a shift in sizing.

Remember, no one sees the size on the tag but you! Yes, you are looking to transform something that no one else can see, but this inward transformation has little to do with your size at all. Instead of chasing a particular size, allow your body to respond naturally to your new eating habits. You will lose weight and keep it off if you establish focused eating habits. Seek physical and spiritual health, not a clothing size.

It Takes Time to Develop a Fitness Habit

Habits take time to develop. In fact, it will take you an average of 66 days to develop a fitness habit. We are all familiar with habits. Think about some of your most essential habits, like brushing your teeth or remembering to take your purse or wallet with you wherever you go. How did you develop those habits?

Most likely brushing your teeth was reinforced by a parent who routinely marched you to the bathroom and stood over your shoulder to make sure it was done. The purse habit, on the other hand, was probably reinforced by a terrifying "oops" moment when you

Part of establishing new weight loss thinking is establishing new focused eating habits and then allowing your body to adjust and change in response to those modifications to your diet.

rushed back to a food court table to discover your purse sitting unmolested where you left it...yep, I've been there.

I've heard it commonly repeated that it takes 3 weeks to develop a habit. When it comes to ingraining a habit, I wondered if 21 days was really enough for a habit to become second nature. I came across a study published in the European Journal of Social Psychology, which concluded that it actually takes an average of 66 days for a person to pick up a new habit.

In a study released in the European Journal of Social Psychology, Phillippa Lally and her team of researchers surveyed 96 people over a 12-week period to find exactly how long it takes to start a new habit.

Over the 12 weeks, the participants chose a new habit and reported each day how automatic the behavior felt. At the end of the period, Lally analyzed the results and found the average time it took for the participants to pick up a new habit was 66 days.[27]

While her results were focused on the time it takes to create a habit, we'll apply this to the time it takes to kick an old one and pick up a better one.

This number makes a lot of sense in light of my weight journey. As I mentioned before, the biggest defining factor for my successful weight loss, after years of failed yo-yo attempts, was the concerted effort to journal my thoughts and reactions to food for a full 50 days.

So, it's not surprising that this research study would conclude that it takes an average of 66 days for a new habit to become automatic. At the same time, I also see some significance in the 3-week model because we often notice perceptible changes at this point. By three weeks, you will no longer notice that you are eating less food. Also, people are more encouraged to continue an activity once they receive the reward of noticeable feedback.

Factors for Developing A New Positive Weight Habit

If indeed it is going to take you just shy of ten weeks to successfully develop a new positive weight habit, it makes sense to consider some factors that will help ensure your success. To develop the two life habits I mentioned earlier (teeth brushing and keeping up with a purse/wallet), habit formation required accountability and reinforcement, whether positive or negative.

Now, let's see how these two factors relate to developing a positive weight habit.

1. Accountability

It always helps to have accountability, which basically involves telling someone about your fitness goals. There is a reason why weight loss programs are so successful. Participants are required to weigh-in at the beginning of each meeting. When a person walks in the door for a meeting, she knows that someone is going to be waiting there with a scale and a clipboard.

There are numerous ways to build accountability into your fitness goals.

- Join an online support group.
- Join a group exercise class.
- Sign up for a fitness competition of some kind.
- Commit to walking with a friend or co-worker.
- Start a blog that chronicles your progress.
- Take pictures of yourself along the way.

2. Reinforcement

Reinforcement is the second essential element for developing a positive fitness habit. There should be self-imposed rewards and punishments for sticking to your routine or falling off of it. You are less likely to stick with something if you have nothing to gain or something to lose.

Practical Step
Possible Rewards and Punishments

Predetermine the amount of weight you want to lose each week (Remember: safe weight loss is from 1.5 to 2 lbs. per week). Place an amount of money in a jar each time you make a fitness commitment. At the end of ten weeks open the jar and count the money...if you have reached your goal, spend it on something you would like, but if you did not meet your goal keep it in the jar for another 3 weeks and count it again. Basically, you will have to live without that money until you meet your goal.

Chapter 9

Develop Habits to Find Your Weigh

I HAVE BEEN TALKING ABOUT the importance of developing habits because I am convinced that habit formation is essential for reaching your goals. Why? It's not the things that you do on a good day when all the planets are aligned and you have a few extra hours to spare that determine your potential for lasting success.

I used to hate it when I would watch a television interview and hear a fit person say, "I eat whatever I want" or "I enjoy working out" in reply to the question, "How do you keep in such good shape?" If you're like me, you have probably been tempted to throw a pillow at the screen or, at the very least, you've explained to the oblivious television that not everyone is as charmed as they are.

But here's the thing: fit people don't have to think about making the right choices because they make the same right choices over and over again regardless of how chaotic their routine becomes. They prioritize their fitness to the point that their behavior becomes habitual. Then, their habits don't have to be considered.

They just do what they have trained themselves to do. That's why you hear fit people say things like, "I eat whatever I want." or "I enjoy working out."

Initially, your new habits will feel restrictive. "No discipline seems pleasant at the time, but painful. Later on, however, it produces a harvest of righteousness and peace for those who have been trained by it." (Hebrews 12:11, NIV) But, as with many of life's skills, the more you practice, the more comfortable you will feel. Eventually, your goal is to get to the point where you automatically perform an action without conscious thought.

Hebrews 12:12-13a goes on to explain that strengthening your feeble arms and weak knees will keep you from wobbling or veering from the path in the future, which is the very problem many of us have faced in our history with food. We start out ok, but then we lose steam along the path and find ourselves stuck eating donuts out in the middle of a metaphorical field; having completely forgotten about the path several miles back.

> Fit people don't have to think about making the right choices and they make the same right choices over and over again regardless of how chaotic their routine becomes.

My Most Effective Fitness Habits

I am sharing a few of my most effective fitness habits. Now, these work great for me and they address some of my key areas of concern—sugar consumption and time management. Yours could be totally different or mine may fit your situation as well.

Here, the aim is to model ways of establishing workable habits that address key areas of concern in my life. In order to establish your own workable habits, you must use your journaling to pinpoint those areas where you struggle the most. While some of these habits will work well for all, others will need to be tweaked to fit your lifestyle and personal needs.

Schedule Set Workout Times and Days

No one will be as motivated for your fitness as you are. If you do not prioritize your exercise times then there will always be something more pressing, more urgent, or seemingly more important to do with your time. Fitness is one of the few activities that you do completely for yourself, so it's easy to see why others' needs can often swamp your exercise routine.

Fitness is one of the few activities you do completely for yourself, so it's easy to see why others' needs can often swamp your exercise routine.

I preset specific days and times for exercise. Then, I do my best to schedule other activities around these times. Of course we all know that life doesn't always happen on schedule. So, for those times when conflicts are unavoidable, I already have a plan for make-up activities.

Choose Filling Snacks

Snacking is important for keeping the metabolism burning and for maintaining consistent blood sugar levels. For me, this is especially relevant for the 5 to 6 hour span between lunch and dinner.

In the past, I would often go for chips or a sweet to satisfy my mid-afternoon hunger. However, because those snacks are essentially empty calories, I would find myself hungry again in a very short time. Then what? Typically, I would go find something else to eat or I would grit it out until time to prepare dinner, then I would eat my first meal standing in the kitchen before the "meal" actually hit the table.

I have learned to make my snacks count. I eat something that will actually stick around for a while. Some of my favorite snacks are nuts, half of a peanut butter sandwich or bananas.

Pre-Pack Your Exercise Bag

Have you ever arrived at the gym only to realize you left your tennis shoes at home? The best time to prepare your exercise bag is the night before you plan to workout. You don't want to worry about it while you are rushing out the door in the morning.

I have a dedicated athletic bag for exercise. As soon as the towels are clean, they go straight back into the bag. I also have a second set of toiletries and even a small makeup kit in there, so I am ready for any eventuality. This really cuts down on my stress and makes going to the gym a lot more workable.

Always Eat Breakfast

When I was younger I hated to take the time for breakfast. I would choose sleep over food any day. But I have read enough to realize how essential breakfast is for jumpstarting my metabolism.

Now, I always eat breakfast. Oatmeal muffins work the best for me and my schedule because they can be made ahead and frozen. That way, I only have to take one out and microwave it for my morning meal.

Pre-Plan When to Eat Dessert

I never eat dessert directly after a meal, unless I am celebrating a special occasion. Sugar has no nutritional value; therefore, I try to remove it from mealtime altogether.

Instead, I allow myself a one to two hour break before eating any dessert. That way I can fully concentrate on it, which helps me to be satisfied with less. This brings me to my last habit.

Cut Down the Size Expectation for Dessert

I have always been a major sweet lover and carb junkie. So naturally, a piece of pie was always one-eighth of a pie…I mean, that's a serving, right? Now I realize that a good bit of the extra weight I carried in previous years was comprised of sugar calories. I just couldn't get enough of desserts.

Today, I still eat dessert and I eat it several times a week, but my size expectation for dessert has decreased dramatically. I often employ the three-bite rule for dessert or, in the case of pie, I eat one-sixteenth. I still get to enjoy sweets, I just don't expect to eat as much as I used to.

Establishing a Workable Dessert Habit

We all are aware of the compelling nature of sugar. Estimates are that the average American consumes 60 pounds of sugar each year...6-0 pounds! I did some quick calculations just to put this number in perspective. That's 92,760 calories worth of sugar. This means, if you take in the average amount of sugar, you have an additional 26.5 pounds that you must either burn off or that gets deposited somewhere on your body.

The average American consumes 60 pounds of sugar each year...6-0 pounds!

This makes a lot of sense to me. I am well aware that the majority of the weight I carried for years was sugar weight. I exercised regularly and did not eat a lot of fried foods; however, I could not keep the sugar cravings at bay! As a result, regardless of any successful weight loss attempt, I would slowly return to a weight that was roughly 20 to 25 pounds heavier than I am now. Hmm, that number is remarkably close to 26.5 pounds.

If you are like I used to be, then a lot of your extra weight is probably from too much sugar. In fact, a lot of us are unable to conceive of a lifetime without dessert. Sugar is such a factor for so many that I felt it needed further emphasis and explanation.

Why Dessert Should Be Separate from Mealtime

I think I've always known that sugar was my biggest weight issue. Thinking back, I realize that I often ate dessert multiple times a day. I had a really bad habit of eating dessert for breakfast. My thinking was if I ate it early enough, then I would still have enough time in the day to burn it off. Of course, the reality was that the memory of that breakfast dessert was long gone by the afternoon, so I would end up eating another piece or two later in the day.

Here's the thing, sugar has no nutritional value. Dessert should be separate from mealtime because our primary purpose for eating meals should be nutrition—our bodies need fuel to operate. So, it makes sense to say that sugar has no place at mealtime.

Thoughts precede actions.

1. Mealtime is for nutrition.

2. Dessert has no nutritional value.

By removing dessert from mealtime, you enforce a new thought process: Dessert does not belong in mealtime because mealtime is for fuel and nutrition. I find I can eat dessert as part of a balanced approach to food as long as I eat it with intention and observe a few rules.

Dessert Rules

1. Never Eat Dessert Directly After a Meal.

It takes a while for the body to register fullness.

Feeling full is a result of your brain reacting to chemicals released when you put food or drink in your stomach. Your brain takes around 20 minutes to register these chemicals. After your meal, the levels continue to rise over 10 to 30 minutes. They stay elevated for three to five hours following the meal, keeping you sated.[28]

If you eat dessert directly after a meal, your body may not have had enough time to register fullness. This allows for a greater possibility that you will eat a larger amount of dessert to make yourself feel full and satisfied.

2. Preserve Dessert for Enjoyment Only.

Preserve dessert for enjoyment only. This goes back to the Entertainment vs. Fuel Dilemma I mentioned in Chapter Six. Food serves two basic purposes: it provides fuel for our bodies or it is a source of entertainment. Since sugar has no nutritional value, it makes sense to remove it from mealtimes when you should be eating food for fuel.

By waiting a few hours after mealtime to eat dessert, you preserve dessert for enjoyment only. This allows you to fully concentrate on the taste and texture, which in turn, helps you feel satisfied with less.

3. *Make an Exception for Special Occasions.*

As a general rule, mealtime and dessert should not meet. Still, rules are meant to be broken… sometimes. Special occasions are…well, special. These are the times that you let your guard down a little bit. Yes, rules give structure and accountability, but we should never feel like we are slaves to them.

Since I started following the dessert rule, I have noticed that special occasions where dessert is eaten as part of the meal experience are really elevated.

Because I don't normally do it, I do feel like I am experiencing a special treat.

Rules give structure and accountability, but we should never feel like we are slaves to them.

Again, we should pause here to remember that food is a blessing. We never want to demonize it; because then, we just set up negative thinking. Instead, we can establish a workable construct for thinking about all the food we eat—including desserts. Then, develop habits to address how we will approach food with focused awareness.

Make a Gameplan

Up to this point we have been slowly peeling back the different layers of our relationship with and thinking about food. When writing this book, I spent a considerable amount of time trying to decide how to organize it. Should I wait to put all practical steps in one place or should I disperse them throughout the book?

I chose to disperse various practical steps throughout the book because I believe in the power of repetition for internalizing ideas, and because food, and our subsequent behavior with it, is such a personal thing. For some, you needed action steps at the mental block level, while others needed steps to address specific excuses.

Consequently, there has been some intentional repetition of ideas and concepts. At this point, we have established a complete framework for helping you to renew your mind and uncover how your mind works with food.

This section is completely practical in nature. While this book is not intended to be a "diet" plan, it essentially follows the steps I took in my journey toward freedom from weight. I guess you could say the practical steps you've read up to this point and will read in this section were my "diet," for lack of a better term.

However, I hesitate to use that term because these are steps that have developed into habits I will follow for life. Unlike a traditional diet plan, these changes represent new habits that I can conceivably follow for the rest of my life without feeling deprived.

Ten Ideas for Lifelong Eating Habits

We all know that weight loss does not just happen without a plan. However, many of us choose drastic measures instead of making small changes to our existing lifestyle. While drastic diets do work in the short run, most of us probably have a personal story of how they failed miserably in the end.

Here are ten habits I have developed:

1. Replace sugared beverages with water or unsweetened tea.

2. Use the "three bite rule" when eating sweets.

3. Pass on chips at lunch and add a slice of cheese to your sandwich instead.

4. Eat sandwiches and burgers with only one bun instead of two.

5. Plan to always have a mid-afternoon snack.

6. Switch to olive oil mayo for prepared salads, but do not exceed 2 tablespoons. Add mustard and yogurt to make your dressing.

7. Pass on mayo for all prepared sandwiches. Choose mustard instead.

8. Stop eating any snack directly from the bag.

9. If you need fries, determine the number you will eat before putting even one in your mouth. Remove the rest from reach.

10. If you need ice cream, eat only one-half cup and then add a sliced banana.

Let's further discuss these ten modifications that can translate into lifelong eating habits.

1. Replace sugared beverages with water or unsweetened tea.

The term "soft drink" refers to any beverage with added sugar or other sweetener, and includes soda, fruit punch, lemonade and other "ades," sweetened powdered drinks, and sports and energy drinks. People who drink sugary beverages do not feel as full as if they had eaten the same calories from solid food, and studies show that people consuming sugary beverages don't compensate for their high caloric content by eating less food.[29]

A 12-ounce can of coke contains 39 grams of sugar and 149 calories, while a Snapple Lemon iced tea has 23 grams of sugar and 100 calories. Compare these numbers with the American Heart Association's recommendation of no more than 6 teaspoons of sugar for women (25g) and 9 teaspoons for men (37.5g) per day.[30] This really gives you a better idea of the sugar content in just one serving of a sugary drink.

Again, the primary issue with sugar is that it has zero nutritional value. Consequently, when you waste 150 calories on a sugary drink, your body receives absolutely no nutritional benefit. What's more, we seldom count our drinks toward our daily food intake. Whereas, we may consciously cut back on something during the day because we ate a donut for breakfast, we are far less likely to even consider the calories from a beverage.

However, if you pass on the sugary drink, you then have 150 calories to spend on a food choice that will actually satisfy your hunger and fuel your body. Bottom line – save the calories for food.

One reason I often go for unsweetened tea is for the caffeine source. Since I don't drink coffee, tea is my primary source of caffeine. Although, there are those who would suggest banning caffeine from your diet as well, that is not a step I am ready to take at this point in my life journey. I guess it's just an issue of picking your life battles.

2. Use the "three-bite rule" when eating sweets.

Most of us have a sweet tooth. Just one stroll down the grocery store aisle attests to that. Couple this with the fact that every main holiday or celebration comes with its own celebratory confection. Unless you are one of those rare individuals who does not really care for sweets, you are always going to be tempted to indulge. So, stop trying to ban all sugar from your life. Instead, take it from the realm of indulgence to that of enjoyment.

The "three bite rule" has been around a long time and it works on a simple principle. The first bite of a rich, decadent dessert is heaven to the taste buds and the second bite is usually just as stimulating as the

Count your drinks toward your daily food intake.

first. But, by the third bite, your taste buds have grown accustomed to the taste, so the food begins to lose its initial appeal.

Calorie wise, three bites seldom pack enough punch to derail your daily calorie expenditure. For sake of illustration, a piece of classic cheese cake from a popular cheesecake restaurant is 710 calories. It is safe to say that three good bites would be about 170 calories. So, you can see how this technique works well to keep the calories in check.

> **By the third bite, your taste buds have grown accustomed to the taste, so the food begins to lose its initial appeal.**

Even so, remember that you can only do the "three bite rule" once in a day. Also, some desserts are so treacherous that three bites could pack quite a calorie wallop. I found a dessert on the restaurant's menu that rolled in at a hefty 1680 calories. Ummmm…those gold standard desserts should be reserved for very special occasions.

3. *Pass on chips at lunch and add a slice of cheese to your sandwich instead.*

In this instance, it is not only important to consider the calorie-count of a particular food, but also the quality of those calories. In the case of chips, a snack-size bag of classic potato chips has 220 calories and 14 fat grams, which is 25% of the daily fat allowance.

On the other hand, a slice of cheddar has about 120 calories and 10 grams of fat, but it also has 7 grams of protein that will help satisfy your hunger for much longer. Also, this choice has some nutritional benefit.

You may be thinking, "Wouldn't it be better to pass on the cheese as well?" A simple answer to that, in terms of fat and calories, is yes. But, successfully navigating food choices for the long-haul involves a give and take. Ultimately, the slice of cheese adds a level of richness to a food while still lending some nutritional value.

Successfully navigating food choices for the long haul involves a give and take.

There are also other cheese choices that are equally satisfying with fewer fat calories, like provolone or feta.

4. Eat sandwiches and burgers with only one bun instead of two.

This is a big one for me because I have always been a huge bread lover. I couldn't envision a life without bread at all, so I decided to put some limits on it instead.

The main problem with bread, especially the white bread in your typical hamburger bun, is that it is classified as a simple carbohydrate. Now, the human body relies on carbohydrates for energy. When you eat carbohydrates, the body breaks them down to create glucose or blood sugar.

However, simple carbohydrates also contain sugar. This means that once your body extracts the energy it needs, it reads white bread almost identically to pure unadulterated sugar. As far as your body is concerned, your hamburger bun might as well be a cupcake, because it breaks down and processes simple carbohydrates and sugars in the same way.

By limiting half of your bread serving, you lower the carbohydrate level and proportionately increase the protein level of a meal.

5. Plan to always have a mid-afternoon snack.

Consider hunger as the archenemy of informed food choices. Plainly put, you just can't get your head screwed on straight when you are hungry. This is the time when you slip up and wreck all the progress you made throughout the day by rushing to eat the first food in sight.

You need to actively plan for a mid-afternoon snack. Your body will need fuel, and unless you plan ahead, you are left with two unappealing options. Either you suffer through the afternoon with the negative effects of rapidly dropping blood sugar or you head to the vending machine to purchase a high-calorie snack.

Preparation is the key. Purchase a variety of high-fiber snacks to have on hand at all times. Then, set a time to have a snack

BEFORE you actually feel hungry. Typically, the best time for snacking is a few hours after lunch.

6. *Pass on mayo for all prepared sandwiches and ask for any rich sauces to be served on the side.*

Mayonnaise is not a friend to the weight conscious person. I actually watched a friend make it from scratch once and that experience definitely discouraged my future consumption. Basically, mayo is a well-blended mixture of pure oil and eggs.

Passing on the mayo for your next burger, will shave about 150 calories and 17 grams of fat right off the top.

In terms of sauces and gravies, always serve them on the side, rather than pouring them on top. This allows you to better control the amount you eat. Then, dip the tip of your fork into the sauce or dressing instead.

7. *Use an olive oil mayo and/or yogurt for prepared salads and yogurt instead of sour cream in casseroles.*

Tuna and chicken salad are two of my favorite lunch options, not to mention potato salad for spring cookouts! So, I had to figure out a way to make these possible. Although I pass on the mayo as a condiment on all sandwiches, it is difficult to think of prepared salads without it.

The difference in the fat and calorie content between full-fat mayo and olive oil mayo is considerable; however, this does not mean that mayo is ever a light option; even the olive oil option is 100% fat.

Because of this, do not exceed 2 tablespoons in your salad. Instead, add mustard and yogurt to finish out your dressing. For some, this new take on prepared salads will require you to adjust your expectation that prepared salads must be white and smothered in mayo.

In terms of casseroles, switch completely to Greek yogurt as an add-in for all prepared casseroles that call for mayo or sour cream. I made this switch several years ago and no one in my family ever noticed the difference, but the difference in calories and fat is huge. For example, an 8-ounce serving of sour cream has 485 calories and 47.5 grams of fat, while an 8-ounce serving of Greek yogurt has 130 calories and 0 fat grams...enough said.

8. Do not eat any snack directly from the bag.

Sitting in front of the television with a bag of your favorite snack chips is the picture of mindless eating. This is a deadly habit for weight control because it throws portion size and focused eating out the window!

You may be thinking, "But, I am eating a healthy snack, so it really shouldn't matter, right?"...Wrong. Even healthy snacking has its limits. For instance, I have lauded the virtue of eating almonds, but here's the thing: nuts are still packed with fat and calories. A serving of 22 almonds has around 160 calories and 14 fat grams. So, while you should eat them for the good trans-fats and hunger-satisfying fiber, you cannot mindlessly down a can of almonds in one sitting.

Make it a habit to remove your snack serving from the bag before you start eating. This allows you to predetermine your consumption. Even if your snack isn't particularly healthy, you may have enough cushion in your daily calorie count to enjoy it anyway, as long as you have consciously considered the cost.

9. *At a restaurant, separate out the amount you intend to eat and remove the rest before you take the first bite.*

Restaurant servings are notoriously large. Again, this is an opportunity to be proactive with your food choices. I love to eat out and I enjoy splurging a little when I do. For instance, I like to eat a few fries when I eat a hamburger. The key is to count out the amount you will eat, then remove the rest from reach.

You know how it goes. You intended to eat only half of your spaghetti, but then you just kept nibbling away at it and before you knew it you were stuffed and the spaghetti was gone. Actually, restaurants have become more accustomed to special requests. It can be helpful to ask your server to bring a to-go box with the meal.

Make it a habit to remove your snack serving from the bag before you start eating.

Another great option is to share your entree with someone else. Not only do you save on the calories, but sharing can save you a considerable amount of money as well.

10. *Remember that an ice cream serving is only 1/2 cup. Make it a banana split.*

We all love ice cream and many of us would find life hard to envision without it, especially when it comes to an evening snack. It is very easy to underestimate the serving size of ice cream. The serving size of ice cream is one-half cup, which is equivalent in size to a medium lemon. Hmm, that's not much is it?

Realistically, few of us are going to be satisfied with such a tiny amount. So, how can we create a more favorable alternative to this little speck of ice cream? First, you need to serve your ice cream in a reasonable-sized dessert bowl. Secondly, you can really amp up the impact of your ice cream by adding one sliced banana. A banana will add about 100 calories to your dessert, making it come in at about 250 calories. But now, you have added a rich source of potassium, Vitamin B6, and fiber to your dessert as well. In addition to the yummy taste, the increased fiber will cause you to feel much more satisfied than if you had eaten the ice cream alone.

Oh, and one last thing to remember about ice creams is that they are not all created equal. Premium grade ice cream has a higher butterfat content and less air than regular ice cream, which typically means about 40% more calories.

There you have my best tips for eating habits that yield real weight results. I think the reason I have found these to be so successful is because I did not have to change anything about my likes and preferences in order to implement them. They are more about tweaking my current lifestyle to include more focused, healthy choices.

What Habits Do You Need to *Find Your Weigh*?

Hopefully, your journaling is progressing well at this point and you have begun to draw connections as you've read through these chapters.

Are there other habits you need to cultivate besides those I've mentioned so far? If so, take some time to jot them down. Make sure you keep things practical and doable. Habits are formed by repetitive action, so you need to pinpoint what specific actions you need to take. Ultimately, the idea is to replace old, destructive habits with workable, focused new ones.

Habits and Action Steps

Habit: _____

Specific Action Steps:

_____

_____

_____

Habit: _____

Specific Action Steps:

_____

_____

_____

Habit: _____

Specific Action Steps:

_____

_____

_____

Chapter 10

Conclusion

Expect Some Bumps Along the Journey

SOMETIMES YOU NEED ENCOURAGEMENT TO just keep going with your weight loss. It is never easy and weight management can be even harder. Give yourself time to settle into the journey until you learn the ropes and begin to feel more comfortable with the terrain.

I hope this book has convinced you that you can *find your weigh*. Hopefully, you have gained some insight into your relationship and subsequent actions with food.

Most of all, I hope you have discovered that viewing your weight loss and subsequent weight management as a journey requires renewed thinking and a new grace mindset. There are no failures on the weight journey, just bumps in the road.

Willpower

How many times have I blamed my inability to control my weight on lack of willpower? I've said it a lot and, most likely, so have you. But here's the thing... willpower is not genetic. Ultimately, weight loss and management comes down to Holy Spirit empowered, conscious choices.

Weight loss requires the will to resist and the power of a resolved mind. But, while you may have the will, you also need God's supernatural power to speak into your weakness from this day forward. You will face less-than-ideal situations in the future and you will be tempted to give in, once again, to the lure of food.

There are no failures on the weight journey, just bumps in the road.

Regardless of any other habit you may have decided to implement, there is still one habit that should be considered one-size-fits-all...if you find yourself in a dark place, step back into the light. "This is the message we have heard from him and declare to you: God is light; in him there is no darkness at all. If we claim to have fellowship with him yet walk in the darkness, we lie and do not live by the truth." (1 John 1:5-6, NIV) The best time to step back into proper habits is right after you realize you have stepped out.

It has to be a step-by-step journey. Small daily decisions and behavior changes can make a difference for the long haul.

- If you've had a setback, pick yourself up and keep going.

- If you have plateaued well short of your ultimate goal, keep going.

- If you've lost the majority of your weight, it can be extremely unnerving and scary to know what to do next; keep going.

The longer you persevere, the more confident you will become. The more confident you become, the more natural your new habits will seem. The more natural your eating habits seem, the less you think about them. The less you have to think about your eating habits, the more they become a part of you. The more they become a part of you, the less you remember your old journey. The less you remember your old journey, the more you can embrace your new one; keep going!

Final Thoughts

I AM SO GLAD YOU chose to take this journey with me. I consider it an honor that you would allow me to step into your world for this brief time.

In essence, this book represents a very personal journey that I traveled to finally achieve freedom over food. Quite frankly, it is a freedom I never would have considered before I started the process.

If this book has also helped you to step into a new freedom over food, I hope you'll take a moment to share it or leave a review to make it easier for others to find.

I had prayed so many times, asking God to help me get the weight off. In retrospect, I realize that my prayer was answered on multiple occasions through various diet strategies.

It wasn't until that November day that I finally realized I had been praying for the wrong thing. I didn't need an answer for getting the weight off; I needed insight into why I put it on in the first place!

Isn't that how we often come to God, if we ever come to him at all? We pray when we're in a pinch or we need something fixed. Basically, we go to God when we've run out of options to deal with life's challenges.

If He comes through, then our dependent relationship is quickly forgotten. If he doesn't answer in a way that we expect, we just figure he never heard us in the first place or didn't care enough to answer.

But, is there more to this relationship between God and us than just calling up a quick list of wants or complaints when life doesn't seem to be going the way we want it to?

I talked a lot about freedom in this book and I so treasure my new-found freedom over the heavy burden of weight. But, as disappointing as my weight struggles have been in the past, I can honestly say I never believed that my weight defined my self-worth or value.

Early in life I understood and accepted the premise that my life has worth and meaning simply because it bears God's signature. God created me uniquely to live and love. Then, he promised he would be with me during life's ups and downs. How did he choose to do that? He sent his son. Jesus lived on this earth and became acquainted with all the challenges I face every day. Then, he willingly died to save me.

So many times, we humans choose to separate ourselves from our creator and forge our own way. It doesn't take much to see the consequences of this decision. We don't live in peace with others or ourselves; instead we live in a world marked by hatred, jealousy, war and sickness. Even scarier than these, we risk an eternal separation from God.

I think we all seek purpose, happiness and inner contentment. I like to think that we are all searching for something to fill our God spot—that place that can only be satisfied by a relationship with the one who put us together in the first place.

When Jesus came into the world over 2,000 years ago, his life was marked by the extraordinary—his birth, life, death and resurrection. Just before he died on the cross, he cried out, "It is finished!" Three days later he rose again in victory, bringing hope and true freedom to all who trust in him.

Because I have chosen to trust in what Jesus did for me, I never feel like I have to tackle life on my own. This freedom gives me confidence and hope to face life head-on knowing that I can trust God to guide my steps.

I hope you also experience this same freedom. If not, but you feel you would like to explore this further, I encourage you to talk to someone who you know has a relationship with Christ.

Also, I would love to hear from you. Feel free to contact me through the "Get in Touch" tab on my website, www.thefabjourney .com or e-mail me at shelliebowdoin@thefabjourney.com.

Shellie

Appendix

50-Day Journal

Pick a consistent time to write in your journal each day. Typically, this time works best in the evening after you have consumed all your food for the day. Also, feel free to write down thoughts throughout the day while they are fresh.

Each person needs to work out a plan that is best for her. Don't worry how long or short your entries are. The important thing is that you start making connections between your thoughts about food and your behavior with food.

In addition to blank space, I also include my own journal entry for the corresponding day. I began journaling for the purpose of documenting my weight journey. Consequently, some of my insights were written with the intent of explanation or information as they were revealed to me. It will become evident that this journal ended up becoming the launching pad for this book.

Keep in mind that every concept in this book was developed from insights I gained from my 50-day journal.

You can choose to approach this feature in one of two ways. Either you can read it after you record your own thoughts for the day or you can use it to spark your thinking if you are having trouble coming up with anything to write for that day.

Reflection questions are included at the end of each week to help you sum up your thoughts and draw out any patterns that you may have revealed or uncovered.

I have also written a companion video Bible study. I encourage you to pick that up as well. It will lead you through the book and the journaling process.

Remember that everyone's journey is different. The things that stood out to me may or may not seem relevant to you in your situation or they may effectively mirror your own thoughts. There is no right or wrong way to figure out how your brain works with food. It's up to you to *find your weigh*.

Journal Entry	**DAY 1**

I begin again but with a new idea: making a life long choice about food. rather than a diet. Man, Lord, I really need your help in this area, but I've been locked into yoyo dieting for so long, I want to be free ~ to make wise, clean choices - Lord help Change & redeem my mind

Shellie's Entry (November 17)

DAY 1. *I just decided last night...I am doing this thing! Originally, I told myself that I would wait until after the New Year to start the process. I mean, who wants to be on a diet through the holiday season! But then it hit me...if I wait until then I will most likely have at least an extra 5 pounds to deal with! I just can't bear going through numerous photos of worthy occasions only to look back on the pictures and think, "I don't want to be that round, middle-aged woman!"*

FURTHER REFLECTION

| Journal Entry | **DAY 2** |

Lord, I confess I'm hungry but I want to keep honoring you through my food choices but that blasted hunger pangs make eating clean hard. Your wisdom is what I need to rely on. May it be stronger than my own selfish will

Shellie's Entry

DAY 2. *I just caught myself thinking, "Thank goodness I almost made it through Day 2. Obviously I am not in autopilot mode yet, but I did come to an interesting and helpful realization today. If I chose to cheat on "the diet," then I am actually making the choice to cheat on myself...on my goals. "The diet" is only a tool for me to reach my goals, so it won't care whether I cheat or not. My goals, on the other hand, can be completely derailed by cheating. I need to see cheating as something personal.*

FURTHER REFLECTION

Journal Entry	**DAY 3**

Lord,

Change my perspective about food. Rather than think of do not this & do not that, think of my food choices as acts of freedom Col. 2:23. Man, that is such a different way at looking at food. Lord, I need Your Holy Spirit to change

Shellie's Entry

DAY 3. *Ok, my munchie time is definitely in the evening after dinner. That compelling urge to snack hits me about 3 hours after the meal. It is essential to be prepared and that's where almonds really come in handy. Here is where I give a shout-out to the almond as the king of snacks. Almonds are full of nutrients, fiber, and protein, as well as healthy unsaturated fats. One serving of 23 almonds is about 160 calories. For now, I have been eating about 6 almonds to tide me over till dinner and then I have been eating 10 almonds and 10 chocolate chips in the evenings. This girl needs just a pinch of chocolate to get through the day.*

FURTHER REFLECTION

my mind away from don'ts to do's! Amen

Journal
Entry | **DAY 4**

*Lord help me understand
You are a God of incredible
mountain moving. Would
you remove this mountain of
fat as I choose better foods,
live in the garden of your
boundaries, & renew my mind
in your Word*

Shellie's Entry

DAY 4. *Half way through Week One...I am putting in all the work, but have yet to see any visible reward....at the same time I know this is the most crucial time for a successful cutback. Any future success will be built on the foundation of this week. My body is going through a withdrawal from excessive carbs, sugar, and fat. I need to visualize a better, more healthy, and yes, thinner future.*

FURTHER REFLECTION

| Journal Entry | **DAY 5** |

Shellie's Entry

DAY 5. *Ok, so tonight was pizza delivery night...I love pizza! With Herculean effort I restricted myself to the smallest piece and the crust of a second piece. I will count this as a victory. That's the thing with cutting back; it's a collection of small victories that will win the battle of the bulge.*

FURTHER REFLECTION

| Journal Entry | **DAY 6** |

Shellie's Entry

DAY 6. *An entire day at home can be a scenario for a diet disaster. I am aware that I often eat out of boredom. This does not pose as much of a problem on busy days, but when I am just hanging out at home, it can become a real issue. Here's the thing...there is no magic remedy or piece of advice that's keeping me from raiding the refrigerator now at 3 o'clock in the afternoon. It comes down to a simple decision. Who or what is in charge of the food I put in my mouth today? Am I in charge or am I leaving the food to make the decisions for me?*

Well, today also proves that there are times when you do not have a choice over the food. Then, you just have to play with the hand you're dealt. We attended a community festival this afternoon and I ended up eating something I would not have eaten at home.

FURTHER REFLECTION

Journal Entry | **DAY 7**

Shellie's Entry

DAY 7. *I made it to the end of Week One! All in all I would call this week a huge success. One thing that stands out to me is that it is ok to feel hunger. So much of the time I work overtime to make sure I never feel it, but I have realized that a little hunger will not kill me. To be honest, I still do not prefer to feel hunger, so I am learning to keep healthy, low-calorie snacks on hand. But, I also do not have to abandon all self-control when I find myself too far between meals.*

FURTHER REFLECTION

Weekly Reflection: Week 1

1. What time of the day are you most vulnerable to snacking? You need to be aware of those times when you are more likely to fall to temptation.

2. Describe how you felt physically this week. This is an important step in learning to listen to your body.

3. Take a moment to think back on any of your successes or failures with food. Jot them down here.

4. If you did experience a failure this week, take a moment to write down the scenario. Can you recall any special circumstances or any self-talk before or after?

5. Think back over your week. What was the biggest factor that would send your thoughts straight to food?

Journal Entry	**DAY 8**

Shellie's Entry

DAY 8. *One week under my belt and I am so tempted to step on the scale to check my progress. BUT, I am staying away. I took some time to think back on my last few attempts to shed some weight and I realized that the scale has been my primary cause of failure...but why? Nothing is quite as discouraging as soldiering through a successful week of self-control only to look down at a number that represents little or no progress!*

You see, the scale can only measure your actual weight at any given moment. It doesn't take hormones into account. It doesn't know that you are retaining water because you took in a little too much sodium. Regardless of the reason, middle-agers are constantly fluctuating in weight, which means you can never know what to expect from the scale. This time I am avoiding the scale for a full 3 weeks.

FURTHER REFLECTION

Journal Entry | **DAY 9**

Shellie's Entry

DAY 9. *It just occurred to me that I did not think about "the diet" once today. I ate right and stayed on track, but I didn't feel like I was depriving myself in any way. This means I am hitting the sweet point when my body starts to go on autopilot and the worst is behind me. Now, I just need to keep this ship on course and follow the game plan.*

FURTHER REFLECTION

| Journal
Entry | **DAY 10** |

Shellie's Entry

DAY 10. *As I mentioned yesterday, there is a point when you eventually hit autopilot because your body is no longer rebelling against the new, sleeker diet. At this point it can be tempting to further restrict calories in order to speed things up. This can actually be counterproductive because too few calories can send the body into starvation mode. In essence, your body will start holding onto its fat stores in order to protect you from starving. Um, I definitely do not want to hold onto anything extra when it comes to fat! I need to remember that slow and steady will yield the best results.*

FURTHER REFLECTION

Journal
Entry | **DAY 11**

Shellie's Entry

DAY 11. *So, today was Thanksgiving and no, I was not a paragon of self-control. There will be days like this when you do not succeed despite your best intentions. So, what does this mean? Do I give up? The answer is a resounding no! I will not allow one day to define my whole effort. Quite frankly, I can speak with experience on this point because I have fallen to this exact scenario in the past. But maybe this is the time when I should put some of my "maturity" to good use, pick myself up and just keep on going.*

FURTHER REFLECTION

Journal Entry | **DAY 12**

Shellie's Entry

DAY 12. *Alright, today I am back on track. It is becoming clearer to me that the true key to weight loss and management is in the mind. Of course, weight gain is caused by excess food; however, I am the one who ultimately makes the choice of what, when and where I eat. I like this idea... I have a choice. If I overeat one day, I can choose to right things the next day without heaping on unwanted feelings of failure and discouragement. Just get back on track: finished and done.*

FURTHER REFLECTION

Journal Entry | **DAY 13**

Shellie's Entry

DAY 13. *I had an encouraging moment today. I put on a blouse that felt considerably looser than it was a few weeks ago. Clothes are really the best gauge of dieting success. Unlike the scale that can be affected by many different factors, clothes respond to inches lost, which is the true indicator of weight loss.*

FURTHER REFLECTION

| Journal Entry | **DAY 14** |

Shellie's Entry

DAY 14. *Here I am at the end of Week 2! I feel quite accomplished to have made it this far. So, what kernels of wisdom have I garnered over the last weeks? It is not insignificant that the United States ranks number one in obesity in the world. Americans have expendable income, which allows them to spend more discretionary funds on entertainment. Consequently, this leads them to seek out further ways to be entertained. What does all this have to do with food and me? Plainly put, I eat to be entertained, rather than for nourishment.*

I eat when I am bored. I eat to celebrate. I eat to socialize. I want to be entertained and dazzled by my food! It's time to shift my thinking and stop looking for food to be the star of the show. When I am bored, I need to read a book. Now, it is unrealistic to say that I can replace the celebratory or social function of a shared meal, but I can teach myself to focus more attention on the company than the entree.

FURTHER REFLECTION

Weekly Reflection: Week 2

1. Have you stayed away from the scale this week? If not, how did you feel when you looked down at the number?

2. How did your body feel this week? Did you notice any positive changes?

3. Were you tempted to overly restrict your calories this week (this is common for people after they have gotten past the initial week of physical withdrawals)? If so, do you think this is a pattern you can sustain for the long haul to reach long-term success?

4. Have you had any setbacks this week? If so, what can you learn from them?

Shellie's Entry

DAY 15. *The dawn of week three...Today I endured a particularly strenuous day at the gym. Mondays are typically lethal because the instructors want to make sure that everyone starts out the week on the right foot. I always give my all when I exercise, so that I can receive maximum benefits because if I slack off, I am only cheating myself.*

For me, it has always been easier to exercise than to cut back on food. Now, I am trying to teach myself to see both practices as a package deal, rather than mutually exclusive.

FURTHER REFLECTION

| Journal Entry | **DAY 16** |

Shellie's Entry

DAY 16. *Tonight I hosted a get-together with some friends who all brought snacks to share. This was my first opportunity to put my new resolve to the test. I actually found it quite enjoyable to focus my time and attention on my friends and the conversation instead of the food. But, that doesn't mean that I couldn't eat anything, I just chose to sample a few things and I found that I was quite satisfied with that.*

FURTHER REFLECTION

Journal Entry | DAY 17

Shellie's Entry

DAY 17. *I felt a little more munchie today than usual. I was hit by the perfect storm of a 2-hour exercise session this morning and holding off dinner for my daughter to return home from a late practice. However, my morning exercise easily burned an additional 500-calories, so I think I am still on good footing.*

There are some important lessons I should keep in mind from today. First, I should plan ahead to eat some additional protein on my heavy exercise days. Second, if I want to have a "little" splurge now and then, I should do it on the days that I have had some good exercise. Third, I need to realize that it's ok to eat a little more on days like this without second-guessing myself.

FURTHER REFLECTION

| Journal Entry | **DAY 18** |

Shellie's Entry

DAY 18. *I was awakened last night with night sweats, a relatively new condition in my bag of tricks. Thankfully, I am not waking up in a pool of sweat as I've heard some do, but I was uncomfortable enough to remain awake for about an hour and a half. Then, on top of that, my discomfort was compounded by screaming hunger pangs. I just ignored them and comforted myself with the thought that the growling signified that my digestive system was operating at optimum efficiency.*

FURTHER REFLECTION

Journal
Entry | **DAY 19**

Shellie's Entry

DAY 19. *I played mental ping pong today as I passed by a fast-food restaurant. It's a feeling I recognize all too well; a craving comes to mind and then I volley the thought back and forth trying to justify it to myself. Of course the craving was intensified by the fact that I was starving on my way home from the gym. In the end I did not cave in, largely because I realized that tonight would likely be pizza night.*

I think that today's experience may be a good way for dealing with future moments like this when I am no longer cutting back. I considered the craving in light of what I would be eating for the rest of the day. If I had decided that I could eat less in the evening to compensate for the mid-day splurge, I would have indulged. I feel that give-and-take and balance will be an essential part of maintaining my weight loss.

FURTHER REFLECTION

| Journal Entry | **DAY 20** |

Shellie's Entry

DAY 20. *Today I need to address a huge culprit for the expanding waistlines of middle-aged women...stress eating. So, what do we have to be stressed about? How about empty nest and the major life changes that this can bring or aging parents to name a few. While the list is long I will mention one issue that is especially real for me. This year I said goodbye to my firstborn as he left home to go to college. At this point it has been almost four months since I have seen his smiling face.*

Yes, this has caused significant emotional stress for me, at times on a very conscious level and at others it rumbles just below the surface. Unfortunately, I have turned to food to bring me comfort over the last few months. Now, I am trying to address my feelings and emotions about this new transition as it relates to my eating. I have to internalize the fact that food will never fill the void left by his absence.

FURTHER REFLECTION

Journal
Entry | **DAY 21**

Shellie's Entry

DAY 21. *I just saw a picture of myself that was posted on a social media site. The picture was taken yesterday and I am pleased to say that I could visibly see the difference these three weeks have made. So, tomorrow will be my first scale day in three weeks. Regardless of the number I see, I need to remember that my body is changing and embrace the progress I have made. Ha, can you tell that I'm scared?*

FURTHER REFLECTION

Weekly Reflection: Week 3

1. Go try on an article of clothing that was too tight when you started your journey 3 weeks ago. How did it fit and how do you feel?

2. Are you too entertainment focused with your food? Describe some times when you looked to food to entertain you.

3. Is there an eating habit that you are performing now that you know you cannot sustain for life? Why is it unsustainable? What changes could you make to the habit that could make it sustainable?

4. Are you developing any new habits that you think you could sustain for good? If so, what makes them workable for you?

Journal Entry | **DAY 22**

Shellie's Entry

DAY 22. *I weighed today and the scale showed a mere 2 pound loss after three weeks of hard work. Normally, this would have sent me into a downward spiral of negative self-talk, but I can tell this journey is really starting to change my mind set. Realistically, I know that I am on my menstrual cycle this week, which translates into serious water retention. What's more, I am slowly conditioning myself to rely more on how my clothes feel, rather than looking for the magic number on the scale. And yes, it would be nothing short of magic to stand on the scale at the precise moment that I am not retaining water either because I am at the end of my cycle, the middle of my cycle, or because I had too much sodium for dinner last night!*

FURTHER REFLECTION

Journal
Entry **DAY 23**

Shellie's Entry

DAY 23. *Today I had to eat fast food for lunch, which definitely makes things more challenging. But difficult does not mean impossible. Regardless of the place, I am learning to make the best choice wherever I am. Since I am a carb junkie I know I need to eliminate bread whenever possible, so I ate my burger with only half a bun, no mayo and no cheese. I find it easier to stick to a diet plan by modifying foods that I enjoy from time to time, rather than limiting myself to a really narrow range of foods day in and day out.*

FURTHER REFLECTION

| Journal Entry | **DAY 24** |

Shellie's Entry

DAY 24. *My son is flying home from college tonight for Christmas break. We haven't seen him for four months and I am bursting with anticipation. In celebration of his return I baked his favorite chocolate layer cake. It's sitting on the counter awaiting his return. I guess you could say it is filled with a mother's love.*

Baking a cake in the middle of a diet may seem counterproductive; however, I am really not feeling an intense draw to dive in. I have already thought it through and I will have a few bites to join in the fun, but I won't indulge. Ultimately, this scenario brings home an important point for this journey. Life does not stop because I am on a diet, nor do I have to isolate myself from food or the enjoyment it brings. Instead, I will choose to stay away from the cake after my initial bites and watch my son enjoy his taste of home.

FURTHER REFLECTION

Journal Entry | **DAY 25**

Shellie's Entry

DAY 25. *Busy schedules can really make it tough to get to the gym, but there are still ways to incorporate exercise into your daily routine. I had to go to the mall today, so I intentionally parked my car in the parking space that was the farthest from the entrance.*

FURTHER REFLECTION

Journal Entry	**DAY 26**

Shellie's Entry

DAY 26. *I am away from home today on a company retreat. For lunch, the retreat center prepared a buffet lunch for our group. There weren't a lot of diet items available on the buffet, so I did my best to make the best choices I could. Unfortunately, our bodies are not wired to give us credit for what we could have eaten. Although I may have shown great restraint by not going for the alfredo pasta, my body is still going to register the calories of the fried fish I ate instead. But this is just part of the real-life journey. Life cannot always be lived in perfectly controlled situations.*

FURTHER REFLECTION

Journal
Entry | **DAY 27**

Shellie's Entry

DAY 27. *Today, I was again away from home and in a situation where I did not have control over the menu. There really weren't any diet friendly choices available, so I chose to hold off on lunch rather than eating really fatty foods. My head was pounding by the time I finally found something to eat. That was a tough one. I am still unsure if I should have made a different decision. I made it this time, but I definitely don't think depriving myself of food is the best choice and my body made sure to let me know that it did not appreciate it.*

FURTHER REFLECTION

202 ~ Find Your Weigh

Weekly Reflection: Week 4

1. Have you learned to find the silver lining when you are required to exert yourself (Fit people find ways to naturally work movement into their days.)

2. How is your mental game going (are you still battling with negative self-talk)? Do you still find yourself going back and forth with whether to eat something that you know you shouldn't?

3. Have you started naturally making a mental plan when you know you will be faced with temptation (preparation is always the key)?

4. Are there still emotional situations that immediately trigger thoughts of food as a way of escape or comfort?

Journal Entry	**DAY 28**

Shellie's Entry

DAY 28. *Here I am at the end of the month. There is a distinct feeling of accomplishment with making it this far, but I still have further to go. I took my measurements today and I am making progress. I have set goals based on my measurements at this point rather than a goal weight. The important thing about my goal is that it is attainable. I am not trying to match any particular size from years gone by. Instead I am targeting a size that will allow me to be fit and no longer look heavy in pictures. I will stop dieting when I reach my target measurements regardless of what my weight is at that point.*

FURTHER REFLECTION

Journal
Entry | **DAY 29**

Shellie's Entry

DAY 29. *Today, I made chicken pot pie for my son's first home-cooked meal since returning home from college. In keeping with my cutback approach of adjusting my portions instead of making separate food for myself, I ate some pot pie for dinner, but avoided most of the crust.*

One of the biggest lessons I am learning on this journey is that the biggest weight loss battles are won in your head. Here is one trick that works for me: determine how much you would want, if you could have all you want, then eat a fourth of that. This allows you to go back for the other fourth. In the end, you have still only eaten half the amount you would have originally eaten. This trick really works. That pot pie was so good and going back for seconds just made me feel more satisfied.

FURTHER REFLECTION

Journal Entry | **DAY 30**

Shellie's Entry

DAY 30. *I bought some large gifts today at the mall. I didn't really think about how I was going to get them to the car until they were bagged and ready to go. Unfortunately, the car was parked a long way from the store, so I had no choice but to load up and carry them. By the time I finally reached the car I was sweaty and exhausted. However, I soon realized that the experience had given me an unexpected burst of exercise. Daily exercise is a necessary element of weight loss, but that doesn't always require a sports bra and a class at the gym. We can actually build in opportunities to move more by doing simple things like parking our car in the farthest parking space from the door.*

FURTHER REFLECTION

Journal
Entry | **DAY 31**

Shellie's Entry

DAY 31. *My body has adjusted to considerably lower amount of sugar. However, I am not really a proponent for doing away with it all together. I see yummy sweets as one of the good things in life, so I have no desire to give them up entirely. Instead, I am trying to teach myself to enjoy them in manageable amounts.*

I just had the three yummiest bites of apple pie and ice cream tonight after dinner. It is surprising to me how satisfying this small amount was. This practice is commonly called the Three Bite Rule and it is an extremely effective way to get the pleasure from food without the guilt. The rule operates on the idea that the first two bites activate the pleasure centers in the brain; however, by the third bite, the pleasure response begins to weaken.

FURTHER REFLECTION

| Journal
Entry | **DAY 32** |

Shellie's Entry

DAY 32. *There is really nothing exciting to report today and that is something that characterizes this whole journey. After the initial jumpstart, there really aren't any real bells or whistles. Instead, it's just a daily choice to make the right decision despite daily temptations. It does get easier, but it still boils down to willpower and a decision to take control of your own body.*

FURTHER REFLECTION

Journal
Entry | **DAY 33**

Shellie's Entry

DAY 33. *Tonight, I knew we were hosting an office dinner complete with a seafood buffet. To keep the calories down I concentrated primarily on the salad bar and grilled fish instead of heavy sauces or carbs-laden side dishes.*

FURTHER REFLECTION

| Journal Entry | **DAY 34** |

Shellie's Entry

DAY 34. *So tonight was pizza night again. I have already mentioned that pizza is difficult for me to resist and tonight was no exception. It is very hard for me to stop at two pieces. Pizza is definitely a trigger food for me.*

It's good to know what your trigger foods are because it helps you to develop strategies to keep from overindulging. For example, I intentionally choose the smaller pieces and I eat mine with a fork and knife. Above all, I try to maintain perspective. If pizza really is one of my favorite foods, then maybe it's ok for me to eat a little more of it than I should as long as I am towing the line with my other food choices.

FURTHER REFLECTION

Journal
Entry | **DAY 35**

Shellie's Entry

DAY 35. *We enjoyed a lovely evening out with several other families tonight. I found it wasn't too hard to make a lighter choice for dinner. The basket of tortilla chips was a little harder to resist; however, I did find it easier to manage by taking out a few and eating them from a plate. This helped me avoid mindless eating and gives me a better idea of how much I ate.*

FURTHER REFLECTION

Weekly Reflection: Week 5

1. What ways have you learned to modify the food on hand to make it a healthier option?

2. Are you finding that the scale is rewarding your efforts from the last month? Do you still feel like the number on the scale somehow measures your self-worth?

3. At this point, have you learned any lasting lessons the hard way?

4. Are you developing a growing satisfaction with your routine or do you consistently feel unsatisfied?

5. You have been going long enough now to see some results. At what point do you think you will be satisfied with your size? Are you still focused on a particular number?

Journal Entry | **DAY 36**

Shellie's Entry

DAY 36. *Some days, my appetite is really strong, while I seem to find myself quite satisfied with small amounts of foods on other days. I am learning to be more in touch with what my body needs on any given day. If I don't feel particularly hungry, then I don't force myself to eat. Likewise, I allow myself a little more grace on the days I feel hungrier. Still, I make sure that I eat three times a day with little snacking, which helps me maintain consistent blood sugar levels.*

FURTHER REFLECTION

Journal Entry | **DAY 37**

Shellie's Entry

DAY 37. *Yesterday, we had family pictures taken and today I got to view some of the proofs. Unlike the picture that propelled me into this journey over five weeks ago, this picture made me smile. I did not look at the picture and immediately see the weight. Instead, I saw a happy mama surrounded by those she holds most dear...great moment!*

FURTHER REFLECTION

Journal Entry	**DAY 38**

Shellie's Entry

DAY 38. *So, today was Christmas Eve and do you want to know what I did? I ate the foods I enjoy eating at Christmas! I don't think this will hurt me one bit. Did I go crazy? No I didn't, but I also didn't count every bite either.*

I am finally wrapping my head around the fact that food is not my enemy, nor does it have any power over me unless I choose to let it. Instead, food is a necessary fuel for my body on most days, as well as a fun and exciting element of important life and family occasions on others.

FURTHER REFLECTION

Journal Entry | **DAY 39**

Shellie's Entry

DAY 39. *Today, we celebrated Christmas. I did eat moderate amounts of some special foods, but I did keep my eating in check. However, I also had some significant intestinal issues to contend with. It is amazing how fast the body adapts to clean eating! Even in small amounts, some of these rich holiday foods have really wreaked havoc on my body. This really hits home how damaging a steady diet of fats and sugar can be to the body.*

FURTHER REFLECTION

<table>
<tr><td>Journal
Entry</td><td>DAY 40</td></tr>
</table>

Shellie's Entry

DAY 40. *It just occurred to me that I seldom have to reach for the antacids these days. Before I started on this journey, heartburn was a constant companion, especially when I laid down at night, not to mention the times I would be awakened from my sleep by a wave of indigestion. Actually, my indigestion had progressed to a point that it was causing me significant pain. Yet another incentive to keep moving forward!*

FURTHER REFLECTION

Journal | **DAY 41**
Entry

Shellie's Entry

DAY 41. *One technique has been particularly helpful over the last weeks of my journey. I call it bite trading. This is a technique that I have started using when I go out to eat with my family. I have always found it difficult to pick from the lighter items on the menu when I know that I could choose something much more satisfying (i.e., rich and calorie laden) for the same price.*

With bite trading, I do choose the more sensible item, but then I trade a small portion of it with someone else in my family in exchange for a few bites of their food. That way I still get a taste of the richer food without all the unwanted calories. Tonight, our family went out to a BBQ restaurant. I ordered the grilled chicken breast and then traded some for a few bites of my daughter's pulled pork.

FURTHER REFLECTION

| Journal Entry | **DAY 42** |

Shellie's Entry

DAY 42. *I have been suffering from hormone headaches the last few days. It is really tempting to want to snack more when my head hurts in a misguided attempt to ease the pain. In the end I did discover one thing that would help and that was a cup of tea. I am currently away from home and my normal routine. I have been drinking mostly water to offset any extra snacks I may have eaten. While this is an excellent move, it also means that I have not been drinking as much unsweetened tea as I do at home...end of story, worse headaches. It's not always easy.*

FURTHER REFLECTION

Weekly Reflection: Week 6

1. Have you discovered any new mind hacks that help you feel more satisfied with your new portions?

2. List your trigger foods. Can you realistically be around your trigger foods without losing control or do you need to stay away?

3. Have you been listening to your body for cues of when to eat or are you still eating by the clock? If so, take note of how you feel at "mealtime." Are you really hungry or eating by habit?

4. Rate how you are dealing with entertainment eating (great) 10 – 1 (not in control). If you are scoring on the low end, what habits do you need to develop (e.g., decide what you will eat ahead of time, eat a healthy snack, always eat salad first with dressing on the side, etc.) to be more in control?

5. Have you found yourself making any excuses this week? Are you owning your decisions and your behavior with food?

Journal
Entry | **DAY 43**

Shellie's Entry

DAY 43. *I got a new wrist fitness tracker device for Christmas. I have used it for two days now and I really like having a visual reminder of my activity level. It gives me a little extra boost to move around a little more each day. The typical trackers set a 10,000 step goal, which translates to roughly 5 miles depending on your height. This doesn't mean that I don't have to watch what I eat, but activity will be the key to keeping it off.*

FURTHER REFLECTION

| Journal Entry | **DAY 44** |

Shellie's Entry

DAY 44. *An essential element of this journey is learning to take responsibility for myself and my own decisions. In doing this I now say that there are no excuses, but bad excuses. Yes, I will inevitably make mistakes that I must own up to and move on, but I don't have to make excuses for them.*

Over the last two weeks I have been unable to meet my normal gym schedule due to family obligations and gym closures. In the past I would have allowed these days to pass with hardly any exercise; however, I am not making excuses this time. I have been out walking almost every day. Sometimes it has been more intentional and other times I have capitalized on shopping trips or outings to get moving.

FURTHER REFLECTION

Journal
Entry | **DAY 45**

Shellie's Entry

DAY 45. *A new year has dawned and I am so thankful to have started this journey! I have come a long way and my mindset has really shifted. I could actually look at a table of calorie-laden snacks without feeling overwhelmed. What's more, I enjoyed a moderate amount of food without feeling guilt or shame. Food is a blessing meant to be enjoyed!*

FURTHER REFLECTION

Journal Entry	**DAY 46**

Shellie's Entry

DAY 46. *I ate lunch at a friend's house today. It did not occur to me until after the fact that I had not even considered the amount I was eating. However, the good news is that I ate and enjoyed a well-balanced, healthy portion without calculating or planning every bite. This is the goal! I want to be aware of what I eat without having to keep every single bite in my mind. The old me would immediately revert to old, poor habits the second my attention was diverted, so this is real progress.*

FURTHER REFLECTION

Journal Entry | **DAY 47**

Shellie's Entry

DAY 47. *I decided to do something new and challenging today. I started my first blog about the weight journey. I think this will be a great way to build accountability into my life. Also, it will take some of the emphasis off of myself, which is a danger with this whole enterprise. There is nothing wrong with turning some of your focus toward yourself and your own well-being, but you don't ever want to get to the point of self-absorption.*

FURTHER REFLECTION

| Journal Entry | **DAY 48** |

Shellie's Entry

DAY 48. *Yesterday and today are good examples of knowing when to eat for fuel and when to eat for entertainment. Yesterday, I did not feel exceptionally hungry. So, I ate small portions at each meal to fuel my body for the day. However, this evening we had friends over for dinner to celebrate one of my son's last night's home before returning to college. We had a nice meal and I was able to enjoy it with my friends and family. I also knew that my light day yesterday would help to balance out my calorie intake.*

FURTHER REFLECTION

Journal
Entry | **DAY 49**

Shellie's Entry

DAY 49. *Today was my son's last day with us before returning to college. I won't see him again for another eight months. No amount of food is going to ease that pain and I know that. Tomorrow, it will be time to pick back up with my gym routine. Exercise is actually a better stress reliever than food.*

FURTHER REFLECTION

| Journal Entry | **DAY 50** |

Shellie's Entry

DAY 50. *Interesting that my milestone day would also be a day of heartbreak as well. This morning we put him on the plane back to college on another continent. I won't get to see him again for another eight months. Of course, the tears have flowed freely, but then I had to pick up and move on. I did go to the gym for a strenuous workout and, yes, it did help to relieve some of my stress and it gave me something positive to do with my restless energy. When stress arises, get moving!*

FURTHER REFLECTION

Weekly Reflection: Week 5

1. Take time to list some positive habits you have developed over the last weeks.

2. Are your new habits becoming more automatic?

3. Now, list any weaknesses you still need to deal with.

4. How do you feel emotionally? Are you optimistic about your future with food?

5. Be honest with yourself. Are you invested enough in your new habits to stop journaling? If the answer is no, then you may want to consider repeating the journaling process.

Journal Entry | **DAY 133**

Shellie's Entry (April 1, 6 months later)

DAY 133. *I am feeling more at home in my skin as I approach 6 months. I am far less consumed by weight, food, or thoughts of food. One thing I have realized is that my body only needs food when it needs it. That may sound strange, but it is a huge departure from how I used to think about food. I used to think it inconceivable not to eat exactly at prescribed eating times and I also used to think I had to have certain amounts to feel satisfied. I am finally starting to listen to my body cues from it.*

FURTHER REFLECTION

Notes

1. "The Diet Industry: A Big Fat Lie," Bloomberg Business, accessed April 18, 2016, http://www.businessweek.com/debateroom/archives/2008/03/the_diet_industry_a_big_fat_lie.html#share

2. Martin B. Katan, Ph. D., "Weight-Loss Diets for the Prevention and Treatment of Obesity," *New England Journal of Medicine* 360, no. 9 (2009): 923-5. DOI: 10.1056/NEJMe0810291

3. Ibid.

4. Ephesians 5:22-23

5. "How Your Body Shape Changes with Age," *About Health*, last modified April 29, 2015, http://longevity.about.com/od/agingproblems/a/How-Your-Body-Shape-Changes-With-Age.htm

6. "2015 Porshe 918 Spyder," Cars.com, accessed May 3, 2016, www.cars.com/porshe/918-spyder/2015/snapshot/

7. "Typical American family earned $53,657 last year," *CNNMoney*, accessed May 3, 2016, money.cnn.com/2015/09/16/news/economy/census-poverty-income/index.html

8. "What Is the Body Fat Percentage of Fitness Models?," Livestrong.com, last modified May 15, 2015, http://www.livestrong.com/article/400397-what-is-the-body-fat-percentage-of-fitness-models/

9. "Did poor workmanship sink the Titanic? Physicist claims missing rivets were crucial to 'cascade' of events that sank liner," *MailOnline*, last modified April 2, 2012, http://www.dailymail.co.uk/sciencetech/article-2124038/Did-poor-workmanship-sink-Titanic-Physicist-claims-missing-rivets-crucial-cascade-events-sank-liner.html

10. "What the Heck is Clean Eating?" *abcNews*, accessed April 18, 2016, http://abcnews.go.com/Travel/what-the-heck-is-clean-eating/blogEntry?id=18887507&ref=http%3A%2F%2Fwww.google.com.ph%2F

11. "Nourish Your Noggin: What Foods to Avoid and Why," brainline.org, accessed April 18, 2016, http://www.brainline.org. content/2012/06/nourish-your-noggin-what-foods-to-avoid-and-why_pageall.html

12. "Obesity and Overweight," Centers for Disease Control and Prevention, accessed May 3, 2016, www.cdc.gov/nchs/fastats/obesity-overweight.htm

13. "Is Fat the New Normal?" *WebMD*, accessed May 3, 2016, www.webmd.com/diet/obesity/is-fat-the-new-normal

14. "Food and Eating: An Anthropological Perspective," Social Issues Research Centre, accessed April 18, 2016, http://www.sirc.org/publik/food_and_eating_9.html

15. "About The United States Healthful Food Council," United States Healthful Food Council, accessed May 3, 2016, ushfc.org/about/

16. "Small Plates Lose Weight," *Food & Brand Lab*, Cornell University, accessed April 29, 2016. http://foodpsychology.cornell.edu/discoveries/large-plate-mistake/

17. "Food Addiction," *WebMD*, accessed April 18, 2016, http://www.webmd.com/mental-health/eating-disorders/binge-eating-disorder/mental-health-food-addiction

18. "Mind Over Matter: Effects of Stress on Metabolism," *Huffpost Healthy Living*, last modified January 13, 2013, http://www.huffingtonpost.com/caroline-j-cederquist-md/sandy-weight-gain_b_2100796.html

19. "Serving Sizes and Portions," National Heart, Lung, and Blood Institute, last modified September 30, 2013, http://www.nhlbi.nih.gov/health/educational/wecan/eat-right/distortion.htm

20. "Portion Perfect," *Woman's Day*, accessed April 18, 2016, http://www.womansday.com/health-fitness/nutrition/a3251/portion-perfect-27486/

21. "Insufficient Sleep is a Public Health Problem," Centers for Disease Control and Prevention, last modified September 3, 2015, www.cdc.giv/features/dssleep/index.html#References

22. "Sleep and Weight Gain," *WebMD*, accessed April 18, 2016, http://www.webmd.com/sleep-disorders/excessive-sleepiness-10/lack-of-sleep-weight-gain?page=2

23. "This is All You Really Need to Know About Staying Hydrated," *Greatist*, last modified July 2015, http://greatist.com/fitness/hydration-during-exercise

24. "Don't like plain water? Here's how to get your 8 glasses a day," *Discover Good*, accessed April 18, 2016, http://www.discovergoodnutrition.com/2012/09/plain-water-get-your-8-glasses-a-day/

25. "What's the Best Time to Exercise?," *WebMD*, accessed April 18, 2016, http://www.webmd.com/fitness-exercise/whats-the-best-time-to-exercise

26. "Some Physical Activity is Better Than None," CardioSmart American College of Cardiology, accessed April 18, 2016, https://www.cardiosmart.org/News-and-Events/2014/04/Some-Physical-Activity-is-Better-Than-None

27. "Scientists Say It Only Takes 66 Days to Change Your Life, If You're Strong Enough," *Elite Daily*, accessed April 18, 2016, http://elitedaily.com/life/motivation/need-stop-bad-habit-need-66-days/784244/

28. "How to Know When Your Stomach is Full & to Stop Eating?," *SFGate*, accessed April 18, 2016, http://healthyeating.sfgate.com/stomach-full-stop-eating-3080.html

29. "Sugary Drinks," Harvard T. H. Chan School of Public Health, accessed April 18, 2016, http://www.hsph.harvard.edu/nutritionsource/healthy-drinks/sugary-drinks/

30. "Added Sugars," *American Heart Association*, accessed June 9, 2016, http://www.heart.org/HEARTORG/HealthyLiving/HealthyEating/Nutrition/Added-Sugars_UCM_305858_Article.jsp#.V1i8P5F97IU

Made in the USA
Monee, IL
15 October 2020

45027675R00146